STAY SLIM FOR LIFE

New, Revised Edition

STAY SLIM
for LIFE

Diet-Cookbook for Overweight Millions

IDA JEAN KAIN
and
MILDRED B. GIBSON

GARDEN CITY, NEW YORK

Doubleday & Company, Inc.

Library of Congress Catalog Card Number 66-17428
Copyright © 1958, 1966 by Ida Jean Kain
All Rights Reserved
Printed in the United States of America

Contents

PART III
CALORIE CHART – TABLES – INDEX

OUR THANKS

The authors are indebted to Dr. Benjamin T. Burton, an Associate Director of the National Institute of Arthritis and Metabolic Diseases, National Institutes of Health, for assistance on the technical points in Chapters 1 and 4.

We especially wish to thank Eugenia Hatcher, who contributed so generously of her time and considerable culinary talent.

We are grateful to Dr. Bernice K. Watt of the Agricultural Research Service, U. S. Department of Agriculture, and to Rose Kerr of the Fish and Wild Life Service, U. S. Department of the Interior, for their indispensable help with the food values.

And finally, we wish to thank our husbands, Dr. Fred F. Beach and Dr. Kasson S. Gibson for their ever-present help and encouragement.

THE AUTHORS

I

The Way Out of
Our Fattening Fix

Chapter 1

WALK DOWN A NEW
SLIMMING PATH

IN THIS land of plenty everyone needs to take a fresh approach to weight control. On-again, off-again dieting is not the way to live happily slim. Through research, science has discovered the way to eat to build healthy leanness. The slimming science is to avoid a major overload at any one time.

If for years you've been trying to hold the weight line on just one ample meal a day, change your eating pattern. The modern way of slighting breakfast, going light at lunch, and eating a big meal at dinner is oddly at variance with the way nature uses fuel for energy. Aside from the fact that the evening is likely to be the least active part of the day, there is another, less understood factor involved. The excess fuel taken at one big meal is shunted into another metabolic pathway, and this is an obligatory pathway into fat.

The overload might be compared to the nightly rush-hour traffic jam. When all the traffic cannot get through, the overflow is shunted into side roads. When the body is unable to cope with an overload through its conventional channels of burning food for energy, nature is obliged to switch to another way of dealing with the excess fuel. In this process, fat is built up as a by-product.

EAT TO BUILD LEANNESS

The plan of eating to build healthy leanness holds out an exciting promise. Until the past few years not much has been known about how the rate of calorie ingestion can alter the way foodstuffs are metabolized. When food is apportioned in small, easily handled amounts, energy is provided at an even rate and hunger is controlled more effectively. The body is not overwhelmed with too much food at one time, and thus the laying down of excess fat in the tissues is avoided. With three moderate meals a day, plus protective pickups in between, you can build a lean, lithe body.

WHAT ABOUT CALORIES?

Does the emphasis on avoiding the overload mean that calories count more at one time than another? On the weight score, calories count the same at all times. Excess calories lead to overweight, regardless of when they are consumed.

It is important to differentiate between weight and fat. The body is a work machine for which food is the fuel. The food eaten yields energy and the amount of energy is measured in calories. Individual energy requirements are also expressed in terms of calories. All excess calories are stored, but one of the major factors in determining *how* the calories are stored depends on the meal pattern. On the identical number of calories, when you take an excess of fuel at one big meal, you set the stage for shunting that excess into body fat. This in turn leads to a disproportionate amount of your weight being in fatty tissue.

HOW MUCH OF YOUR WEIGHT IS IN FAT?

The new approach to the weight problem is directed toward body composition. Body weight and body fat are not necessarily directly related to each other. Obesity is a condition in which a disproportionate amount of the weight consists of body fat. You can be too heavy by the scales, but lean if your weight is principally protein tissue (muscle) and body structure, rather than fat. However, if you look fat, you are probably carrying an excessive amount of fat. For moderate degrees of overweight, it is difficult to know how much of the weight is due to fat. You can be overly fat without being overweight. Some sedentary persons can be obese at normal weight or even underweight. Body composition is the basis for determining obesity, regardless of weight. So the significant question is this: What proportion of your weight is in body fat?

Check with your doctor. Weight tables define the normal limits of variation of weight for height and include a weight range based on frame. But there are no tables that measure body composition so as to indicate the proportion of fat.

Much of the excess fat in the body is right under the skin. Your doctor can measure the thickness of the layer of fat with calipers. The best places to measure are: the triceps, that spot on the back of the upper arm; the subscapular skin fold under the shoulder blade; the abdomen and the midriff. These areas are good indices of all-over body fatness.

For practical purposes, the pinch test gives a fair indication. The layer of fat beneath the skin should be between one-fourth and one-half inch thick. Take a deep pinch of skin on the side of the body just over the lower ribs. Between thumb and index finger, pick up a fold of flesh. If the fold is thicker than one inch, this is evidence of excess subcutaneous fat.

When too much of your weight is in fat, you are in potential trouble. It is excess *fat* that is associated with the chronic degenerative diseases. Ask your doctor.

If you are overweight generally, reduce. Change your food habits and your pattern of eating, cut calories, and burn your excess fat with exercise. Exercise will also help you to have a firm, well-toned body.

RESEARCH FINDINGS

A giant stride was taken in nutrition research when Clarence Cohn, M.D., Director of Nutritional Sciences, Michael Reese Hospital in Chicago, conducted the initial research on nibbling versus big-meal eating in experimental animals. It was found that the little white rats that ate all their daily quota of calories in two large meals deposited more fat and retained less protein. The other group, on the same diet mixture, eating whenever they wanted to, deposited less fat and built leaner bodies.

What about the weights of the two groups? As long as the same quantity of food was consumed, the weights were identical. (Total calories determine body weight.) The relative proportion of fat was greater in the big-meal eating group. Of the greatest significance was the fact that the cholesterol levels of the big-meal eaters was *double* that of the nibblers. These research findings have proved to be a real breakthrough in nutrition.

Further scientific experiments were conducted by Dr. Guy F. Hollifield and Dr. William Parson of the University of Virginia School of Medicine. The animals that were allowed access to food for a limited time only soon learned it was now or never to get their rations. In the time allowed they gobbled up all the food in sight and ate a greater quantity of food than the nibbling animals. The "gobblers" weighed 30 percent more than the nibblers and had far more fat in their tissues.

What can be learned from the nibbling versus big-meal eating experiments?

1 – On the same calorie total, overloading at big meals leads to laying down a disproportionate amount of fat in the tissues. The new tissue added is fat.

2 – Moderately small meals, supplemented by scientific pickups, lead to a higher protein body composition and a leaner body.

3 – A meal pattern that encourages overeating at any one time leads to more fat storage in the tissues and to a higher cholesterol level.

From nutrition studies it appears that overweight individuals tend to do more of their overeating at one period, specifically in the evening. When the major portion of the day's calories are eaten between six at night and bedtime, trying to reduce is a discouraging, never-ending struggle.

Obviously, you and I cannot emulate the daylong nibblers, but we can alter our pattern of eating so as not to cram the major portion of the calories into one huge meal. It makes abiding good sense not to overeat at any one time. Aside from avoiding the overload, eating smaller meals definitely helps to cut appetite down to size.

On smaller meals you retrain your "appestat." Hunger pangs do not come as soon. Before long you get accustomed to eating less at a meal; then the temptation to overeat diminishes. Stop overeating and glory be, you stop wanting to overeat.

IS FOOD MORE FATTENING IN MIDDLE AGE?

Overweight is the big problem in middle age. The common complaint is: "I don't eat any more now than I ever did, but food seems to get more fattening."

There is no mystery about it. In middle age we come up against a frustrating law, to wit: the law of calorie reversal. Our calorie requirements lessen as the years go by. Also, we take life easier.

Ironically, as monetary income climbs, fuel requirements decline. On the sunny side of twenty-five, when it is often a struggle to make ends meet, we can burn calories galore. In middle age, when we are more comfortably fixed financially, nature economizes on calorie spending. By the time we can afford prime ribs au jus and flaming cherries jubilee, such gourmet fare is too fattening. Then we worry about which meal the next excess pound is coming from.

Calorie requirements decrease with age. Here are the facts: After twenty-five we burn 5 to 7 percent fewer calories with each passing decade. By age fifty, which as everyone knows is just high noon of life, we require 12 to 17 percent less fuel than we did in our salad days. By age sixty, the human power plant requires roughly 20 percent fewer calories to run on than at age twenty-five.

To compound the problem, in middle age our physical exercise lessens perceptibly. The tendency is to become more sedentary. There it is, as the years fly by, nature runs the body on less fuel, and you and I ease up on physical activity. When fuel requirements decline markedly, food seems to get more fattening.

Unfortunately, appetite, which is the desire for food, doesn't diminish, not in like degree anyway. Also, there is the lure of the palate—food tastes so good. The food habits established in our physically active years tend to persist, and pounds pile on with the birthdays.

Americans are in a dilemma. We have an unprecedented abundance of delicious food available the year around, plus convenience foods with built-in maid service. But we are no longer calorie spenders. Weight control is the balance between calories eaten and calories expended in all forms of energy.

Underexercise and overeating appear to go together. Sedentary people who get little exercise do not seem to have the natural on-and-off switch in the brain that regulates their desire for food intake in accordance with their actual needs. In any weight-control plan, mild, regular exercise is as essential as limiting calories.

EXERCISE TO BE FIT, NOT FAT

Pushbutton living is forcing fat on us. Over the years the weight picture has changed startlingly. The most alarming change is the widespread overweight in all age groups. Today we have chubby children, roly-poly preteens, and fat teenagers, in addition to the millions of middle-age overweight men and women. There is no question about it, our sedentary mode of life has robbed us of the natural way to control weight.

Studies have shown that obese children do not eat so much more food than normal-weight youngsters, and some of them eat less, but the fatties are inordinately inactive. On the playground they stand around instead of participating.

It's a mistaken notion that exercise always increases the appetite. The overweight youngster will eat heartily, exercise or no. With physical activity, the food is burned for energy and the youngster feels peppier and happier.

Physical exercise is the best way to take advantage of the natural responses of the body to burn fuel for energy. Since exercise is no longer built into day-to-day living, we have to take time, indeed make time and devise ways to get enough exercise. Research into how the body functions shows that exercise plays a role not only in weight control but in relieving stress. The rewards of a small amount of regular exercise are almost beyond measure.

What kind of exercise is needed? Any kind that uses the big muscles of the body. Walking is a natural. Golf, gardening, bowling, tennis, swimming, and dancing are all excellent activities. Calisthenics as a means of keeping in tone is coming back in vogue. Although not so much fun as sports activities, calisthenics tones the muscles, prevents sagging, and rebuffs fat.

Muscular activity increases calorie expenditure more than any other single factor. The following chart gives the energy cost in calories *per minute* of an adult weighing between 140 and 155 pounds. These figures were taken from "Human Energy Expenditure," by Drs. R. Passmore and J. V. G. A. Durnin of Scotland (*Physiological Reviews*, Vol. 35, October 1955).

ENERGY EXPENDITURE

	Energy Cost *Cal. Per Min.*
At Ease	
Lying at ease	1.4
Sitting at ease	1.6
Sitting writing	1.9
Sitting playing cards	2.1
Standing at ease	1.8
Action	
Standing drawing	2.3
Washing and dressing, man	2.6
Washing and dressing, woman	3.3
Romping with children	3.5
Household Tasks	
Hand sewing	2.0
Light laundry	3.0
Ironing	4.2
Polishing	2.9
Routine Activity	
Driving a car	2.8
Driving a motorcycle	3.4
Gardening, weeding	5.6
Gardening, digging	8.6
Gymnastic Exercises	
Abdominal	3.0
Trunk bending	3.5
Arm swinging, hopping, etc.	6.5
Walking	
Walking 2 m.p.h.	2.9
Walking 3 m.p.h.	4.0
Walking 4 m.p.h.	5.2

Recreation – Involving Moderate Exercise	Energy Cost Cal. Per Min.
Dancing	
Foxtrot	5.2
Rhumba	7.0
Waltz	5.7
Cycling, 5 m.p.h.	4.5
Horseback riding, trot	8.0
Bowling	4.4
Golf	5.0
Archery	5.2
Tennis	7.1
Swimming, recreational	6.5
Swimming, competition racing	11.0
Skiing, moderate speed	10.8

WHY FADDY DIETS FAIL

Everybody loves to eat and nobody wants to be fat. So the search for a magic way to take off weight goes on and on.

The latest diet to entice the overweight population is variously called the Air Force Diet, the Astronaut's Diet, and the Drinking Man's Diet. (None of these diets is sponsored by the U. S. Air Force Medical Service.)

The furor over this diet will wane eventually, for in the long run it simply won't work. The reducing success of any diet depends on calories. However, since some version of the calories-don't-count type of diet is periodically revived, let's solve the mystery.

The popular versions of the diet appear to allow unlimited amounts of rich, fatty foods, plus alcohol, with the single restriction being on carbohydrates. To add to the illusion of magic, the fast weight loss in the beginning is sometimes greater than can be accounted for on the calorie score.

What is the mystery? Water loss, initially. In shifting to a low-carbohydrate, high-fat, high-protein regime, tissue water is lost. In an effort to get rid of the fragments of incomplete fat metabolism, the kidneys must mobilize body water for this purpose. Trying to wash out the imperfectly burned end products and combat acidosis, the kidneys excrete more water than usual. This process dehydrates body tissues, and weight is lost—temporarily. Dehydration is not oxidation, and water loss is not fat loss.

Initial weight loss and subsequent loss are two different things. If the dieter continues to lose after the dehydration phase, it will be because he is sated with fatty foods before he has eaten his maintenance quota of calories. Weight loss will *not* be due to any "magic" connected with either low carbohydrate or high fat.

In a mystery story the plot is always devious so as to direct attention away from the real culprit. In the low-carbohydrate diet, pleasing emphasis is placed on the permitted abundance of rich foods, not on the calorie interdictors. The way foods are composed, when carbohydrates are severely restricted, total calories are slashed drastically.

On the 60-gram carbohydrate limitation the dieter must forego sugar, assorted pastries, pies, cakes, candy, and all sweets. Fruits, fruit juices, cereals, potatoes, starchy vegetables, and bread are all rigidly restricted. It doesn't take much detective work to account for the missing calories on the eat-all-you-want plan. You want only so much fat and protein, and you can't have sweets and starches. All those pleasure-giving foods which are left out lower the boom on calories.

Dieters, don't be fooled. If you really increase fats and proteins as these faddy diets claim is permissible, you cannot lose —you are sure to gain.

WHAT'S WRONG WITH THE DIET PLAN?

Any diet that appeases hunger and reduces weight is bound to create a sensation. There is no question but that high fat and high protein give satiety. Since appetite is satisfied, what is wrong with this diet and why is there so much controversy about it? Why is it not acceptable to scientists, nutritionists, and the medical profession?

The built-in health risks are too great. To satisfy hunger by including an excessive amount of fat in the daily fare is a recognized health hazard. The medical profession is concerned about the consumption of excess dietary fat and its relationship to heart disease, the number-one killer. When carbohydrates are rigidly limited, the tendency is to eat more fat and protein. In big eaters, the low-carbohydrate diet can be alarmingly high in fat. Most overweights are big eaters.

The claims of miracles for any diet unrestricted in calories are false and misleading. Everybody wants an easy way to reduce, one that is painless and pleasant. But there is no diet in which you get something for nothing.

We have gone through many experiences of altering the proportion of calories that come from the three nutrients, protein, fat, and carbohydrate. When one nutrient is curtailed, the other two are increased. This leads to an unbalanced diet and unsound nutrition.

HOW MUCH CARBOHYDRATE IS NEEDED?

Dieting, to be successful, must engender new hope. If the novelty of counting carbohydrate grams can help to cure your sweet tooth and keep calories within reducing limits, count them. There is nothing wrong physiologically with keeping score on carbohydrates, provided the diet is properly balanced and total calories controlled. If it is a psychological help to keep score, fair enough. Understand, however, that there is no magic in the method, and that it is just another way of limiting calories.

What is wrong is the severe limitation on carbohydrates, for this not only results in a deficient eating pattern but throws the diet out of balance.

On the carbohydrate score: For the normal adult, the Food and Nutrition Board of the National Academy of Sciences, National Research Council, suggests a minimum of 125 grams of carbohydrate a day. In terms of calories, this adds up to 500 carbohydrate calories. Each gram of carbohydrate furnishes 4 calories. Each gram of protein also furnishes 4 calories. Fats furnish 9 calories per gram. Alcohol yields 7 calories per gram.

From the standpoint of nutrition, a significant point is that the term *carbohydrate* makes no distinction between sugar and starch. While the over-all consumption of carbohydrates has dropped since people have become weight conscious, the decrease applies to the starches—potato, bread, cereal, and other starchy foods—more than to sugar. It is carbohydrate in the form of sugar that rushes through the gastrointestinal tract and leaves you hungry again in a short time. This is not true of the starches, for they are utilized more slowly. Also, many of the starchy foods, particularly the whole grains and enriched products, furnish needed nutrients. The food composition table on pages 236–41 gives an easy method for figuring the gram amounts of all nutrients, including carbohydrates.

KEEP NUTRIENTS UP AND CALORIES DOWN

For both reducing and weight control, hold fast to the well-balanced pattern of eating. Foods are made up of various nutrients, or food substances needed to maintain the body in good working order.

The familiar terms *proteins, fats, carbohydrates, vitamins, minerals,* and *water* are nutrient classifications. The way foods are composed, nutrients are "packaged" together in certain foods. For example, milk: among other nutrients, milk provides proteins and needed minerals and vitamins.

The nutritionally important foods are divided into four groups—milk group, meat group, vegetable-fruit group, and bread-cereal group. A well-balanced pattern of eating means that food is selected from each of these four essential food groups. When foods from one group are slighted, a number of nutrients may be in low supply.

Calories are a measure of the fuel content of foods, in terms of *quantity.* However, the term makes no distinction between calories which furnish fuel only and those which contribute essential nutrients.

With calorie requirements diminished as they are in our sedentary way of life, the emphasis must be on *quality.* The expression "keep your calories in good company" applies to empty versus protective calories. Nutritionally speaking, the term *empty calories* applies to foods lacking in proteins, minerals, and vitamins. Sources of empty calories are sugar, some cooking fats, poor-quality baked goods, and alcohol.

Nutrition science is wonderful! Thanks to our modern knowledge it is possible to adjust our energy intake to our maintenance or reducing calorie requirements, without short-changing ourselves on any vital nutrient.

SHUN FADDY FARE

The scientifically planned pattern of eating for weight control is more sensational in positive results than faddy fare ever could be! Look upon protective nutrition not as a diet but as a way of eating for glowing health and more joy in living.

Delicious food need not be fattening fare. The light calorie touch can be given to recipes without detracting from flavor or sound nutritional values. Dietary know-how combined with culinary skill enables us to dine well and slim down any number of excess pounds. Most important, a good state of nutrition, together with desirable weight can be maintained for a lifetime.

Chapter 2

SET YOUR DATE FOR
DESIRABLE WEIGHT

IT'S A fascinating fact that you can set the approximate date by which you can reasonably expect to be down to desirable weight. If you are like most overweight individuals, you want to be slimmer in order to look better. Fair enough. The unexpected reward is that you will *feel* so much better. Desirable weight is the weight that favors good health and long life.

How tall are you and what is your body build? There is no exact pound at which you are "ideal" weight, but there is a zone within which your weight is normal for your structure. Use this rule of thumb: For the ladies—allow 100, 105, or 110 pounds for the first five feet of height, depending on whether you have a small, medium, or large frame. Then add five pounds for each extra inch or subtract five pounds for each inch under five feet. Height is computed without shoes, weight without clothing.

Men can allow 110 pounds for the first five feet of height and five and one half pounds for each extra inch. This is considered right weight for a man with a medium-size frame.

The weight chart on page 234 gives desirable weights for height, and takes framework into account. Weight charts in general use reveal what the weight picture is currently, rather than stating desirable weights.

In judging your frame, you can use your glove size as a guide. Women wearing gloves smaller than size 6, and men smaller than size 8, can be regarded as having a small frame. Women wearing gloves larger than size 7, and men larger than size 9, generally have a large frame. If there is any question about your frame, settle for medium.

What about birthdays and weight? After twenty-five it is *not* desirable to add pounds with the years. At that approximate age, muscular development has been accomplished. The weight that is right for your height and build in the twenty-five-to-thirty age bracket is your healthiest weight from then on. In fact, medical authorities now lean toward the light side of normal weight for senior citizens.

PLAN FOR LOSING ONE TO TWO POUNDS A WEEK

Calorie arithmetic takes the guesswork out of reducing. With nutrition science and toning exercise you can lose one to two pounds a week on three good meals a day, without going hungry or shortchanging yourself on any nutritional essential. This is no idle promise. You can be free of the burden of fat.

The rate of weight loss is set by your calorie deficit. One pound of body fat has a fuel value of 3500 calories. When calories in the daily fare are cut below requirements, nature is forced to draw on reserve fuel stored in excess pounds; thus body fat is used.

Your reducing calorie requirements are based on your maintenance allowance. Recommended Daily Dietary Allowances have been estimated by the Food and Nutrition Board of the National Academy of Sciences, National Research Council. This chart is given on page 235.

For young women who are normally active, calorie requirements have been estimated at 2100 per day. For middle-aged women, the calorie requirements are estimated at 1900 per day. These are for normally active women. For the sedentary worker, an easy way to figure calorie requirements is to multiply your desirable weight by 15. This calorie total represents your maintenance requirements.

Plan your reducing diet on the basis of one-third calories *less* than your maintenance requirements. Reducing diets for women range from 1000 to 1400 calories a day. It is better not to cut calories lower than 1000 a day, unless your physician so advises. Certain foods, aptly termed protective, are known to be superior sources of the nutrients essential to upkeep and renewal of body tissues. It is difficult to include adequate amounts of the essential nutrients when calories are rigidly restricted. On 1000 calories a day, the normally active woman can lose about two pounds a week.

If you are past young middle age, a weight loss of one pound a week is often more desirable. As the years go by, the skin is less elastic and a moderate rate of losing allows more time for skin contraction to keep pace with the shrinkage in fatty tissue. A daily deficit of 500 calories brings a loss of one pound a week, which amounts to fifty-two pounds off in a single year. On 1200 to 1400 calories a day, depending on your age and activity, you can lose one pound a week and enjoy abundant fare.

MAN-SIZE REDUCING DIETS

According to the Recommended Daily Allowances, a middle-aged man requires 2600 calories a day. This allowance is based on the reference man, five feet nine inches tall, weighing 154 pounds, who is moderately active physically.

To figure your maintenance calorie requirements, multiply your desirable weight by 15, if you are sedentary, and by 20 if you are physically active. Note: Excess fat is not to be figured in this estimate. Calculate your reducing calorie allowance at one-third less than your maintenance calories. Reducing diets for men range from 1400 to 1800 calories a day.

It is a mistake to reduce on a crash diet, or to cut your reducing calories too low. True, you could reduce faster, but you would not change your food habits, and the lost pounds would pile back on again with compound interest. Alternate gaining and reducing is not in the interest of health. Among other hazards, recurrent weight gains can cause high blood pressure. Dr. Frederick J. Stare, Director of the Department of Nutrition, Harvard University School of Public Health, has pointed out that it is probably during the process of growing fat that the most damage is done to the blood vessels, particularly the vessels of the heart. Reduce and hold the weight line, and you materially increase your chances for living longer.

INITIAL WEIGHT LOSS UNPREDICTABLE

On a reducing diet the initial rate of weight loss often varies. During the first ten days or two weeks of calorie curbing, the unexpected may happen. You may lose five pounds the first week or your weight may not change for an aggravating two weeks. This seeming paradox occurs when a loss in body fat is accompanied by a temporary shift in water balance. Since water weighs more than the fat it has displaced, the scales could even register a gain. Failure to scale down at the start of a diet is not due to any resistance on the part of the fat, but is caused by water retention in the tissues and variation in water content of the body fat.

As a rule, the more overweight you are, the more you are likely to lose at the start of the diet. With considerable soft fat, there is likely to be more surplus water in the tissues and initial weight reduction can be dramatic. Since a portion of this loss represents water, you will not continue to reduce at this rate. It is well to remember that water retention can occur at any time during the reducing course. Do not be discouraged, the water balance always adjusts and your weight will have come down the predicted amount at the approximated date.

EAT TO BUILD LEANNESS

Whether you need to lose twenty pounds or a hundred and twenty—eat to build healthy leanness. There is nothing mysterious about planning scientific reducing fare. The first rule in a safe reducing diet is to include adequate protein. The word *protein* means "first place," so give protein first place at each meal. Also, include adequate amounts of all the protective foods in the day's total. Fuel can be used from any source—sugar and starch, fats and protein—but repair material comes chiefly from the protective foods.

The foods that furnish complete protein are milk, skim milk and buttermilk, cheese, cottage cheese, eggs, meat, fish, seafood, poultry, and soybeans. Whole grains, peas, beans, and lentils furnish smaller but significant amounts of protein. The balance of the menu is made up of vegetables, fruits, cereal products and bread, and butter or margarine.

In figuring nutrient values, the Food Composition Table for Short Method of Dietary Analysis given on page 236 will be of real help. In this chart, foods of similar composition are grouped together and the mean values for each of the nutrients are given. The advantage of this shortened method is that nutrients can be figured easily and time saved.

Women need 58 grams of protein daily and men 70 grams. However, 85 or more grams of protein are often recommended for reducing diets, for protein has the power to stimulate metabolic processes and stave off hunger pangs.

To control hunger and build a lean, lithe body, eat three balanced meals a day, and have an energy pickup in the late afternoon. When you eat sparingly during the active part of the day, you are certain to overeat at dinner. The excess fuel taken at that meal is laid down as fat in the tissues. With this practice a disproportionate amount of your weight is in fatty tissue.

Also, when you go without food for many hours of the day, you lose out on stepped-up metabolism. Food intake causes an increase in metabolism, known as the specific dynamic action of food. Protein causes the greatest rise. On the same number of calories, dieters lose more effectively when a protein is included at each meal, and when the food is divided rather than eaten at one large, late-day meal.

Zero hour for dieters is apt to be late afternoon, when blood sugar tends to fall. It is an excellent plan to have an energy pickup around four o'clock in the afternoon. This is termed scientific piecemealing. It can save the day and the dieter. The snack should be one that stays by you; it should not exceed 100 to 200 calories, and of course must be counted in the day's total.

Now back to meal planning. The following list of foods provides 1000 to 1200 calories and furnishes an abundance of all the nutrients required for optimum nutrition. It is not a set diet but a food pattern by which you can plan your own reducing fare. On this pattern you can lose one or two pounds a week, keep your esprit, and look and feel years younger.

DAILY FOOD PATTERN

Milk: Skim milk or buttermilk, 1 pint. Or liquefied nonfat dry milk.

Lean meat, fish, poultry, eggs, cheese: 2 to 3 servings. Have 4 to 6 ounces, cooked weight, of lean meat, fish, or poultry. Eat only *lean* parts of meat. Have 1 egg, or ½ cup cottage cheese, or 1 ounce yellow cheese.

Vegetables and fruits: 4 servings or more. Include one dark green leafy or deep yellow vegetable. Most vegetables grown above the ground are low in calories and if no fat is added, such vegetables can be eaten in liberal quantities. The exceptions are corn, winter squash, peas, lima and navy beans. *Fruits:* Include one citrus fruit or juice, plus a second fruit.

Bread and cereals or alternates: 2 to 3 servings. Enriched white or whole-wheat bread in limited amounts can be included. One slice of bread is equivalent to ½ cup cooked cereal, or ⅔ cup of prepared cereal. One medium potato is the calorie

equivalent of 1½ slices of bread; or ½ cup cooked rice, macaroni, spaghetti, lima beans, or a medium-size ear of corn.
Fats: 1 tablespoon of oil, plus 3 level teaspoons of margarine or butter. This amount of fat includes that used in cooking.
Water: An adequate intake of water is extremely important. Eight glasses of water or beverages should be consumed daily.

ENJOY SLIMMING FARE

Eating should always be a pleasure, particularly when calories are curbed. The way to make weight control a natural is to plan meals that are high in satiety but not high in calories.

Certain foods appease hunger more effectively than other foods do, completely apart from the calorie story. The satiety value of a food is a measure of the extent to which a food gives a sense of well-being and satisfaction.

Except for fat, meat has the highest satiety value of all food and therefore "sticks to the ribs" longest. Clear soups and broth, because of the meat extractives contained in them, stimulate the gastric juices and also provide that important feeling of satisfaction.

Fish is an excellent protein food, but lower in satiety value than meat. So, with a fish meal, add a second protein, such as slices of hard-cooked egg, toasted almonds, or melted cheese on the vegetable. Or include cottage cheese with the salad.

It is well to be in the know about potato and bread. The satiety value of these two foods is relatively low. However, when eaten with meat, fish, or chicken, a potato or a slice of bread adds to the satiety of the meal. What happens when you take seconds on these starches? Studies reveal that the satiety value of a meal does *not* rise proportionately when the amount of potato or bread is increased. You would boost the calories without adding significantly to hunger satisfaction. In contrast, the satiety value of meat increases directly in proportion with the amount eaten.

Green vegetables and crisp, crunchy salads provide essential nutrients and bulk. A sense of fullness is part of the normal satisfaction of hunger.

Fats boost satiety, but they also boost calories. To cut calories fast, trim fat from meat and be alerted to hidden fat in gravy, rich sauces, and casserole dishes. Some fat is needed in the diet, particularly unsaturated fat. Use the fat where it is most appreciated, in salad dressings, and for butter or margarine on bread or potato. A half pat of margarine on a baked potato satisfies.

As a finishing touch to a meal, please the palate with a delectable dessert such as fruit, gelatin, or a custard made with nonfat milk and topped with berries.

Be a gourmet dieter, eat slowly and savor food for flavor. The mechanism of satiety takes a little time to be effective. With fast eating it is easy to ignore nature's signal that you have appeased hunger. Fast eating encourages overeating. Overeating in turn enlarges your food capacity and lessens resistance to overeating. You cannot win that way.

Try the high-satiety, balanced, protective diet. You can plan delightful meals and slim down, without going hungry. Dinner's on . . . and it's not fattening!

SHAPE UP WITH EXERCISE

To have more energy and less fat, exercise. The happiest reducers are those who team diet and exercise together. When you diet stringently and shun exercise, something dreary happens to your looks and to your spirits. On too little food you tire easily and practice economy of motion. Sloth sets in, muscles atrophy, and the result is a drawn, depleted look. The bloom is off. There is little to be gained by exchanging fat for sagging muscles.

A small amount of regular exercise is wonderfully rewarding. To tone up as you slim down, take some form of unstrenuous exercise—walk a couple of miles daily, swim, dance, or ease through calisthenics. When it comes to slimming off inches, calisthenics is a definite help.

From the standpoint of shapeliness, the muscles that are neglected in daily living should be exercised. These include the important abdominal muscles which brace the front line, and the lateral muscles which bound the silhouette on the sides. When muscles go soft, the figure loses its clearly defined lines. The triceps muscles on the backs of the upper arms need toning, too.

Exercise tones, tightens, and stops the sagging. With toned muscles you look and feel silken slim and lissome. Furthermore, physical activity is a marvelous release from tension.

If you are a heavyweight, be sure to talk with your doctor about the amount and kind of exercise that will be best for you. Prior to reducing is an excellent time for a physical checkup.

Chapter 3

SOCIAL CALORIES

ENTERTAINMENT is one of life's choice pleasures and eating is a delectable part of the fun of the party. Hearty hospitality is a deeply ingrained part of our American heritage, and perhaps the last fattening frontier to change will be our ideas on social eating.

As hostesses, we like to serve our guests the best. As guests, we enjoy the bounteous repast and want our hostess to know we appreciate her culinary efforts.

Our attitude on social eating hasn't changed greatly. None

the less, etiquette rules are undergoing a subtle but definite change. This has come about as a result of the growing awareness of the dangers of excess poundage.

It is no longer considered a breach of good manners to turn down proffered food or drink. The modern hostess is completely understanding when a guest refuses seconds or even declines to partake of the first helping. Many hostesses make it a point to include some foods which are not too high in calories so that all the guests can enjoy the refreshments. Isn't that what hearty hospitality really means?

PLAN FOR PARTYGOERS

Let's talk about social calories from the dieter's angle. Since much of today's party fare is served buffet style, you can take as much or as little as you please.

At a buffet a good slimming plan is to have a generous serving of the sliced chicken, ham, or meat dish, the tossed salad, sliced tomatoes, or low-calorie relishes. The salted nuts, the hot rolls, and the rich dessert can be unobtrusively passed up.

Even at a dinner party one can tactfully curb calories by declining seconds and slighting the dessert course. When the attitude of the hostess is mature and one honestly doesn't want to overindulge, it isn't difficult.

There is one problem, however, and that is the long-delayed hour of eating at many dinner parties. Appetites get out of control. It is wise strategy to piecemeal with a purpose before going to an affair where the meal is to be served long past your regular hour of eating. Cut ahead of appetite with an energy boost before you leave home. Have a cup of hot bouillon and a wedge of cheese, or a glass of milk or buttermilk, or a hard-cooked egg and a cup of hot tea. A half glass of the formula diet makes a good pickup. Far from being wasted calories, an energy lift serves a double purpose. It saves you from that all-gone feeling which so often sets in before the delayed dinner is finally served, and it keeps you from going overboard on fattening food. The sort of food served at social functions is almost always richer than everyday fare.

Many men and women, because of their professions, must accept numerous invitations to affairs where food and drinks are served lavishly. Those who control their weight, apparently without effort, have a built-in system. Resolute people know what they want, and it is certainly not to pile on excess pounds; therefore, they have made a temperate decision which covers all occasions. A polite "No thank you" is not a matter of will power, it is habit.

Weight control is 90 percent attitude. If you prefer desirable weight to excess food, that attitude prevails and there is no need to make a separate decision over every hors d'oeuvre. When social eating is determined by habit rather than by momentary choice, it becomes a matter of second nature to be moderate.

This is by no means the same as going to a party grimly determined not to partake of the delicious fare. That plan would be doomed to failure, for it accentuates the negative and takes away the fun.

Get a new point of view. Decide to be a gourmet dieter. Only overeating is fattening. If what you really want is to get back your slim good looks and hold the weight line, you will not be tempted to overindulge on party fare. With this new attitude, you will find to your pleased astonishment that you have a built-in slimming system. The power of an attitude approximates magic.

Chapter 4

ALCOHOL AND
THE THINKING MAN'S DIET

EVER since the dawn of fermentation there has been spirited controversy as to whether alcohol can be directly stored as adipose tissue. So alluring is the idea that alcohol calories disappear in some mysterious metabolic process that even intelligent people are tempted to lend an ear to the sweet music of promise. Some version of the "Eat, drink and be merry" diet keeps coming back like a siren song.

No factual solace can be offered with regard to the Drinking Man's Diet. Dr. Philip L. White, nutritionist with the

American Medical Association, had this to say about it: "The Drinking Man's Diet is utter nonsense, has no scientific basis, and is chock-full of errors."

Since alcohol delivers calories the same as food, only faster, the thinking man is forced to conclude that any diet liberally laced with alcohol is sheer Lorelei on the rocks.

Here are the facts: Alcohol has a definite fuel value of 7.1 calories per gram, or approximately 200 calories per ounce. The number of calories in alcoholic beverages depends on the percentage of alcohol, usually expressed as proof. The higher the alcoholic content, the higher the calories. A 100-proof whiskey contains 50 percent alcohol. A whiskey labeled 90 proof would contain 45 percent alcohol; 86 proof, 43 percent alcohol; and 80 proof, 40 percent alcohol.

All such calories must be considered potential weight makers, as alcohol is a sparer of food calories. When alcohol is being burned for fuel, the food calories are not used for fuel and they are converted into fat.

Then, too, cocktails and alcoholic drinks whet the appetite. This leads to peanuts and pretzels, caviar and cheese, or high-calorie tidbits of one kind or another, and on to a hearty dinner. Because of the dulling effect of alcohol on the higher nerve centers, inhibitions are lifted, including calorie caution. However, it is not only because alcoholic drinks stimulate appetite that they are potential weight makers. It is the old adage of two and two equaling four. When alcohol, plus food, boosts the grand total of calories over the top of one's requirements, the surplus calories are stored.

In this modern age it is not realistic to claim that all alcohol calories are taboo if one is to control weight. The moderate use of alcoholic beverages does not contribute as much to obesity as the excessive use of sweets and calorie-rich desserts.

From the nutrition standpoint, alcohol calories are not very worthwhile, for they furnish none of the repair and replacement nutrients needed all life long. Since alcohol is devoid of the protective nutrients, it should not take the place of any essential food.

On a strict reducing diet, limited to 1000 calories a day, no calories can be spared for alcohol if the dieter is to be well nourished. For the dieter on a 1200-calorie diet, the cocktail or highball can take the place of a sweet. Those on a 1500-to-1800-calorie diet can have a before-dinner drink and skip the rich dessert, and if they wish, have a drink during the evening —and still lose weight. The drinks must be counted as part of the day's calories.

That's the story, here's the calorie bill.

WHISKEY, GIN, RUM—1 jigger, 1½ ounces	*Calories*
100 proof	150
90 proof	135
86 proof	130
80 proof	120

COCKTAIL CALORIES

Manhattan
2 oz. bourbon or rye (86 proof)   225
1 oz. Italian vermouth

Martini
2 oz. gin (80 proof)   195
1 oz. French vermouth

Daiquiri
2 oz. rum (80 proof)   180
tsp. sugar, powdered
juice of lime

Champagne cocktail
3 oz.   150

BEER AND ALE	*Calories*
Beer, 12-oz. can or bottle	150
Ale, 12-oz. can or bottle	200

CORDIALS (1 oz.)

Benedictine	110
Brandy	110
Crème de menthe	105
Crème de cacao	75
Cognac	75
Sloe gin	75

WINES (3 oz.)

Port	160
Sherry	135
Vermouth (French)	105
Vermouth (Italian)	165
Table wines: Chianti, claret, Rhine, etc.	75

Chapter 5

SLIMMING MENUS

IMAGINATIVE menus add zest to reducing. By using recipes that have been trimmed of unnecessary fattening ingredients, you can plan appealing meals that are surprisingly low in calories.

The following menus are adaptable for family fare. Normal-weight members can have larger portions of these same foods, plus bread and butter and whole milk. Good nutrition is basically the same for all, the main difference is in the size of the servings and the added trimmings.

The best diet aid is to be aware that it takes a little time to appease appetite. Eat slowly and really savor the food for flavor. With fast eating the emphasis is on filling up, rather than on enjoyment of the meal. The practice of getting up from the table short of that full feeling is the ideal way to train appetite down to proper size. Thirty minutes later you will feel quite content.

In these menus the specialty dishes, written in italics, are included in the recipe section. This taste-satisfying way of eating for fewer calories can do more than anything else to change food habits and help you to stay safe weight for life.

Lifesaver Diet

Mr. and Mrs.

Slimming, Mr.-and-Mrs. style, is twice as easy. The menus are the same, but his servings are a little larger.

Wives often lament that calorie curbing would be quite simple if they didn't have to cook big meals and fix fattening desserts for a hungry husband. And many a husband has been known to express the wish that his wife wouldn't cook such fattening fare—not that he doesn't enjoy the delicious meals, but the trouble is he is piling on so much weight. Unwittingly you may have been encouraging each other to overeat. And it is a sobering fact that on the same eating pattern you will both continue to gain unwanted pounds.

Since the head of the house has lunch away from home on weekdays, the luncheon menus are restricted to dishes that can be ordered. Also a pattern for the carried lunch is suggested.

If either partner loses weight faster than one and a half to two pounds per week, food portions should be increased for that member. Mr. can add 200 to 300 calories to the day's total.

A word to the wives: The success of this slimming venture is largely up to you, for you prepare the meals. With low-calorie recipes, reducing can be a certainty. To keep the pounds off, continue to curb calories in the kitchen.

For young married couples just starting out, bear in mind that prevention of overweight is good health insurance.

SLIMMING MENUS

BREAKFAST		Calories	
		Mrs.	*Mr.*
Orange juice	4-oz. glass	60	60
Egg, soft-cooked	1 egg	80	80
Toast			
Mrs.—1 slice		60	
Mr. —2 slices			120
Jam	1 tsp., rounded	35	35
Coffee, black		–	–
		235	295

LUNCHEON			
"Cream" of tomato soup	1 bouillon cup	105	140
(Mrs. with skim milk)			
Grilled cube steak	3½ oz.	210	210
(½ tsp. fat), on toast	1 slice	60	60
Fruit (for Mr.)	1 serving		100
(fresh, canned or			
frozen)			
Tea or coffee		–	–
		375	510

PICKUP*			
—Late afternoon			
Skim milk or buttermilk	8-oz. glass	90	90

DINNER			
Mixed grill:	1 chop	105	105
Lamb chop (loin—lean			
meat only)			
Liver, calf (floured	1½ oz.	110	110
lightly)			
Baked potato			
Mrs.—½ medium		45	
Mr. —1 medium			90

* Mr. can choose any suitable pickup available, keeping within the stipulated calorie allowance.

		Calories	
		Mrs.	Mr.
Butter or margarine	½ pat	25	25
Green Beans with Mush-rooms and Parmesan Cheese	⅔ cup	45	45
Tossed green salad	1 serving	25	25
French dressing			
Mrs.—½ tbsp.		30	
Mr. —1 tbsp.			60
Apricot Whip	1 mold	35	35
Coffee, black		–	–
		420	495

Total calories for day: Mrs., 1120; Mr., 1390

		Calories	
BREAKFAST		*Mrs.*	*Mr.*
Grapefruit sections, fresh	½ cup	40	40
Canadian-style bacon	2 slices	110	110
Toast			
Mrs.—1 slice		60	
Mr. —2 slices			120
Butter or margarine	½ pat	25	25
Coffee, black		–	–
		235	295

LUNCHEON			
Beef patty, on	3-oz. patty	185	185
Toasted hamburger roll			
Mrs.—½ roll		70	
Mr. —1 roll			135
Cucumber pickles	4 slices	20	20
*Wedge of lettuce with		50	50
Quartered tomato			
Cottage cheese (for Mr.)	½ cup		120
Skim milk or buttermilk	8-oz. glass	90	90
		415	600

PICKUP—Late afternoon			
Swiss cheese	½ oz.	50	50
Apple	½ medium	35	35
		85	85

DINNER			
Broiled Chicken	¼ of 2-lb. broiler	190	190
Choice of: Parsley potato or rice (½ cup)		80	80
Butter or margarine	1 tsp.	35	35
Asparagus with pimiento strips	6 spears	20	20
Carrot curls		10	10
Fruit Nectar Fruit Cup	1 serving	90	90
Coffee, black		–	–
		425	425

Total calories for day: Mrs., 1160; Mr., 1405

* Old-fashioned dressing: vinegar, seasoning, and sprinkle of sugar.

		Calories	
BREAKFAST		Mrs.	Mr.
Orange juice	4-oz. glass	60	60
Hot cereal	¾ cup	100	100
Sugar	1 tsp.	16	16
Milk, whole	½ cup	80	80
Toast (for Mr.)	1 slice		60
Butter or margarine	½ pat		25
Coffee, black		–	–
		256	341

LUNCHEON			
Hot vegetable soup	1 bouillon cup	70	70
Swiss cheese on rye—			
Mustard		–	–
Cheese	1 oz.	105	105
Rye bread			
Mrs.—1 slice		55	
Mr. —2 slices			110
Tart apple (for Mrs.)		70	
Baked apple (for Mr.)			170
		300	455

PICKUP—Late afternoon			
Hot bouillon	1 cup	25	25
Ry-Krisp, seasoned, toasted	2 triple crackers	50	50
		75	75

DINNER		Mrs.	Mr.
Roast beef (sirloin—lean meat only)	¼ lb.	235	235
Baked Acorn Squash	½ squash	75	75
Brussels sprouts with mushrooms	½ cup	30	30
Tomato Aspic on chicory	1 serving	30	30
Baked Custard (low-calorie)	1 custard cup	100	100
Coffee, black		–	–
		470	470

Total calories for day: Mrs., 1101; Mr., 1341

		Calories	
BREAKFAST		Mrs.	Mr.
Grapefruit	½ medium	60	60
Shirred Egg	1 egg	100	100
Canadian-style bacon, broiled			
Mrs.—1 slice		55	
Mr. —2 slices			110
Toast	1 slice	60	60
Butter or margarine	½ pat	25	25
Coffee, black		–	–
		300	355
LUNCHEON			
Slice of juicy roast beef	3 oz.	175	175
on rye bread	1 slice bread	55	55
Tossed green salad		25	25
French dressing			
Mrs.—1 tbsp.		60	
Mr. —1½ tbsp.			90
Ice cream, vanilla (for Mr.)	¼ pint		145
Coffee or tea		–	–
		315	490
PICKUP—Late afternoon			
Skim milk or buttermilk	8-oz. glass	90	90
DINNER			
Spiced Veal Cutlet	3 oz.	230	230
Baked potato			
Mrs.—½ medium		45	
Mr. —1 medium			90
Butter or margarine	½ pat	25	25
Parsley carrots	2	40	40
Celery Stuffed with Cottage Cheese	2 stalks	50	50
Melon-Ball Fruit Cup	1 serving	50	50
Coffee, black		–	–
		440	485

Total calories for day: Mrs., 1145; Mr., 1420

		Calories	
BREAKFAST		Mrs.	Mr.
Ripe banana, sliced, on	½ banana	45	45
Wheat flakes	¾ cup	100	100
Sugar	1 tsp.	16	16
Milk, whole	½ cup	80	80
Toast (for Mr.)	1 slice		60
Butter or margarine	½ pat		25
Coffee, black		–	–
		241	326

LUNCHEON			
Crabmeat Salad			
Mrs.—⅔ cup		135	
Mr.—restaurant			150
Sliced tomatoes and		35	35
watercress			
Bread	1 slice	60	60
Butter or margarine	½ pat	25	25
Cantaloupe	½	60	60
		315	330

PICKUP—Late afternoon			
Hot tea		–	–
Cheese	¾ oz.	80	80

DINNER			
Broiled mackerel or	5 oz.	200	200
bluefish fillets			
Lemon butter (1 tsp.		40	40
butter, 1 tbsp. lemon			
juice)			
Oven French Fries	1 serving	100	100
Green beans	Generous serving	25	25
Savory Slaw	1 serving	45	45
Broiled Grapefruit	1 serving	85	85
Coffee, black		–	–
		495	495

Total calories for day: Mrs., 1131; Mr., 1231

		Calories	
BREAKFAST		Mrs.	Mr.
Orange juice	4-oz. glass	60	60
Ham, thin slice pan-broiled	2 oz.	155	155
Toast	1 slice	60	60
Butter or margarine	½ pat	25	25
Coffee, black		–	–
		300	300
LUNCHEON			
"Cream" of chicken soup (skim milk)	1 bouillon cup	130	130
Chef's Salad	1 serving	205	205
Rye bread			
Mrs.—1 slice		55	
Mr. —2 slices			110
Butter or margarine	½ pat	25	25
Tea or coffee		–	–
		415	470
PICKUP—Late afternoon			
Skim milk or buttermilk	8-oz. glass	90	90
DINNER			
Mushroom Meat Loaf			
Mrs.—1 slice		160	
Mr. —1½ slices			240
Wax beans	Large serving	20	20
Broiled Tomatoes	2 halves	60	60
Hot French bread			
Mrs.—1 slice		60	
Mr. —2 slices			120
Butter or margarine	1 pat	50	50
Fresh peach*	1 medium	35	35
Coffee, black		–	–
		385	525

Total calories for day: Mrs., 1190; Mr., 1385

* Or one-half canned peach.

		Calories	
		Mrs.	*Mr.**
BREAKFAST			
Tangerine juice	4-oz. glass	55	55
Poached Egg Supreme	1 serving	205	205
English muffin, toasted	½	70	70
Butter or margarine	½ pat	25	25
Coffee, black		–	–
		355	355

DINNER—Sunday			
Golden Brown Chicken	½ lb.	215	215
Corn on cob	1 medium ear	70	70
Butter or margarine	½ pat	25	25
Asparagus	6 spears	20	20
Sliced cucumber	½	15	15
Seasoned vinegar			
Angel food cake	2″ wedge	110	110
		455	455

SUPPER			
Open club sandwich			
Rye bread	1 slice	55	55
Mayonnaise	Thin spread	15	15
Mustard	Dash	–	–
Lettuce leaf		–	–
Chicken, meat only			
Mrs.—2 slices (2 oz.)		100	
Mr. —3 slices (3 oz.)			150
Swiss cheese (for Mr.)	1 slice		105
Hot Cocoa (low-calorie)	1 cup	95	95
		265	420

Total calories for day: Mrs., 1075; Mr., 1230

* Mr. can add 200 to 300 calories to day's total.

PATTERN FOR LUNCH TO CARRY

	Calories
Sandwich:	
2 slices bread,	120
lightly buttered	25
Thick filling of lean meat, chicken, or cheese	150
Choice:	
Celery, carrot sticks, small tomato	25
Choice (for Mr.):	
Drumstick, hard-cooked egg, or 1 oz. cheese	100
Choice: Fresh fruit	75
Mrs., 395 calories Mr.,	495

Budget Fare

For the overweight, one of the unhappy facts of life is that low-cost foods are usually high in calories. It takes careful planning to cut costs and calories and at the same time ensure good nutrition.

Protein is the expensive item of the meal. Choose the lean and less expensive cuts of meat, and cook these economy cuts slowly. Prime-grade meat is higher not only in cost, but in calories. Trim fat from meat. Cook all food with a minimum of fat.

Watch for the weekly specials on meat, canned goods, and staple grocery items. Plan the meals around foods which provide grade-A nutrition. Fish, fresh or frozen, is made to order for low-calorie menus. Dry skim milk, cottage cheese, eggs, and fish are a boon to dieters on a budget, for they furnish high-quality protein.

On these budget menus you can be properly nourished, lose one to two pounds a week, and not go hungry.

		Calories
BREAKFAST		
Tomato juice	4-oz. glass	25
Egg, soft- or hard-cooked	1	80
Whole-wheat toast	1 slice	55
Butter or margarine	½ pat	25
Coffee, black		–
		185
LUNCHEON		
Hot beef bouillon	1 cup	5
(use cube)		
Open-face sandwich		
Rye bread	2 slices	110
Swiss cheese	1 oz.	105
Mustard	Thin spread	
Celery	As desired	10
Carrot sticks	12 thin	10
Tart apple	1 medium	70
Skim milk or buttermilk	8-oz. glass	90
		400
PICKUP—Late afternoon		
Skim milk or buttermilk	8-oz. glass	90
DINNER		
Choice:		
Baked ham, lean, or	2 slices (3 oz.)	160
Baked pork chop	1 (trim off fat)	155
Sauerkraut with caraway		
seeds	¾ cup	35
Baked potato	1 medium	90
Butter or margarine	½ pat	25
Grapefruit and Green	1 serving	50
Pepper Salad		
French dressing	1 tbsp.	60
Coffee, black		–
		420

Total calories for day: 1095

Calories

BREAKFAST

Grapefruit sections, fresh	½ cup	40
Hot oatmeal	½ cup	80
Sugar	1 tsp.	16
Milk, whole	½ cup	80
Toast	1 slice	60
Butter or margarine	½ pat	25
Coffee, black		–
		301

LUNCHEON

Omelet	1 egg	125
Rye toast	2 slices	110
Butter or margarine	½ pat	25
Cherry Fruit Salad	1 mold	30
Hot tea		–
		290

PICKUP—Late afternoon

Skim milk or buttermilk	8-oz. glass	90

DINNER

Tomato Bouillon	1 bouillon cup	35
Liver, beef, broiled (lightly floured)	3 oz.	195
Baked potato	1 medium	90
Butter or margarine	½ pat	25
Coleslaw	1 serving	25
Apricots, canned	3 halves, 2 tbsp. juice	85
Coffee, black		–
		455

Total calories for day: 1136

		Calories
BREAKFAST		
Stewed prunes	3 with	65
served on	1 tbsp. juice	
Hot Cream of Wheat	¾ cup	100
Milk, whole	½ cup	80
Coffee, black		–
		245

LUNCHEON		
Tuna Fish Salad	1 serving	140
Bread	1 slice	60
Butter or margarine	½ pat	25
Canned pineapple	2 small slices	90
	with juice	
Hot tea		–
		315

PICKUP—Late afternoon		
Hot Cocoa (low-calorie)	1 cup	95

DINNER		
Cheese Soufflé	¾ cup	225
Whole-wheat bread	1 slice	55
Broccoli	1 large stalk	25
Butter or margarine	1 pat	50
Stuffed Tomato Salad	1 serving	60
Apple Ginger-Upper	1 serving	25
		440

Total calories for day: 1095

		Calories
BREAKFAST		
Grapefruit, fresh, or	½	60
Grapefruit juice	(4-oz. glass)	
Egg, poached, on	1 egg	80
Toast	1 slice	60
Butter or margarine	½ pat	25
Coffee, black		–
		225
LUNCHEON		
Tomato soup	1 bouillon cup	105
(skim milk)		
Chicken livers	3	110
broiled with		
Apricot halves	2 halves	40
Bread	1 slice	60
Butter or margarine	½ pat	25
		340
PICKUP—Late afternoon		
Skim milk or buttermilk	8-oz. glass	90
DINNER		
Ground beef (lean round	3-oz. patty	185
steak), broiled		
Roll, toasted	1 hamburger roll	135
Butter or margarine	½ pat	25
Stewed tomatoes	¾ cup	45
Relishes: celery, radishes		35
and cucumber pickles		
Fresh pear	1	100
		525

Total calories for day: 1180

Calories

BREAKFAST

Tomato juice	4-oz. glass	25
Shredded Wheat	1 biscuit	85
Sugar	1 tsp.	16
Milk, whole	½ cup	80
Toast	½ slice	30
Butter or margarine	½ pat	25
Coffee, black		–
		261

LUNCHEON

Vegetable soup	1 serving	70
Cottage cheese	½ cup	120
Rye toast	1 slice	55
Butter or margarine	½ pat	25
Fresh fruit	1 serving	75
Hot tea		–
		345

PICKUP—Late afternoon

Skim milk or buttermilk	8-oz. glass	90

DINNER

Broiled Ocean Perch Fillets	⅓ lb.	190
Oven French Fries	1 serving	100
Spiced Beets	⅓ cup	30
Salad greens		25
Thousand Island Dressing	1½ tbsp.	22
Peaches with Meringue	1 peach half	60
Coffee, black		–
		427

Total calories for day: 1123

Calories

BREAKFAST

Orange juice	4-oz. glass	60
Hot cereal	¾ cup	100
Sugar	1 tsp.	16
Milk, whole	½ cup	80
Coffee, black		–
		256

LUNCHEON

Grilled Velveeta cheese	1 oz.	90
on rye	1 slice bread	55
Apple and celery salad, with		75
Fruit Salad Dressing	1½ tbsp.	30
Hot tea with lemon		–
		250

PICKUP—Late afternoon

Skim milk or buttermilk	8-oz. glass	90

DINNER

Beef Pot Roast,	1 serving	300
with vegetables		
Tomato and green pepper	1 serving	40
salad, French dressing	1 tbsp.	60
Spanish Cream	1 serving	85
Coffee, black		–
		485

Total calories for day: 1081

Calories

BREAKFAST

Orange-grapefruit juice	4-oz. glass	55
Scrambled Eggs	1 serving	170
Toast	1 slice	60
Butter or margarine	½ pat	25
Coffee, black		–
		310

DINNER—Sunday

Golden-Brown Chicken—	½ lb.	215
Slimming Style		
String beans	Large serving	25
Baked potato	½ medium	45
Butter or margarine	½ pat	25
Celery and radishes	As desired	15
Angel food cake	2″ wedge	110
Coffee or tea		–
		435

SUPPER

Tomato soup (skim milk)	1 bouillon cup	105
Toasted Triscuits	3 squares	65
Swiss cheese	1 oz.	105
Tart apple	1	70
Hot tea with lemon		–
		345

Total calories for day: 1090

Gourmet Meals

These gourmet meals, cooked according to calorie-counted recipes, make eating for weight control a positive pleasure.

Calories

BREAKFAST

Chilled orange juice	4-oz. glass	60
Ham, pan-broiled	2 oz.	155
Toast	1 slice	60
Butter or margarine	½ pat	25
Coffee, black		–
		300

LUNCHEON

Crabmeat Salad	½ cup	100
Tomatoes and watercress	Large serving	35
Hot French bread	1 slice, 2″ thick	120
Butter or margarine	½ pat	25
Melon balls with mint	¾ cup	40
Tea or coffee		–
		320

PICKUP—Late afternoon

Hot Cocoa (low-calorie)	1 cup	95

DINNER

Broiled Chicken	1 serving	190
Carrots and Mushrooms	½ cup	35
Italian green beans with	½ cup	25
toasted almonds	2, split	20
Tossed green salad		25
French dressing	½ tbsp.	30
Dieter's Cheese Cake	1¾″ wedge	115
Coffee, black		–
		440

Total calories for day: 1155

Calories

BREAKFAST

Tomato juice, with lemon	4-oz. glass	25
Poached Egg Supreme	1 serving	205
Coffee, black		–
		230

LUNCHEON

"Cream" of chicken soup (skim milk)	1 bouillon cup	130
Fruit Platter with Cheese	1 serving	190
Melba rounds, toasted	4	36
Tea or coffee		–
		356

PICKUP—Late afternoon

Skim milk or buttermilk	8-oz. glass	90

DINNER

Skewered Lamb and Pineapple	1 skewer	180
Baked potato	½ medium	45
Butter or margarine	½ pat	25
Peas and carrots	½ cup	50
Sliced cucumber	½	15
Mocha Pudding	½ cup	60
Demitasse		–
		375

Total calories for day: 1051

		Calories
BREAKFAST		
Cantaloupe	½	60
Canadian-style bacon	2 medium slices	110
Toast	1 slice	60
Butter or margarine	½ pat	25
Coffee, black		–
		255
LUNCHEON		
Omelet with Fines Herbes	1 serving	200
Green beans, French style	½ cup	15
Grapefruit and Green Pepper Salad	1 serving	50
English muffin, toasted	½ muffin	70
Butter or margarine	½ pat	25
Tea or coffee		–
		360
PICKUP—Late afternoon		
Skim milk or buttermilk	8-oz. glass	90
DINNER		
Roast beef (sirloin—lean meat only)	¼ lb.	235
Baked Acorn Squash	½	75
Asparagus with Mushrooms	1 serving	65
Endive and watercress salad		10
French dressing	½ tbsp.	30
Red raspberries, frozen	4 oz.	110
Coffee, black		–
		525

Total calories for day: 1230

		Calories
BREAKFAST		
Ripe banana	½ medium	45
Shredded Wheat	1 biscuit	85
(crisped in oven)		
Sugar	1 tsp.	16
Milk, whole	½ cup	80
Coffee, black		–
		226

LUNCHEON		
Open-face roast beef	3 oz. lean meat	175
sandwich, broiled	1 slice rye bread	55
Hearts of lettuce		10
Russian Dressing	1½ tbsp.	24
Skim milk or buttermilk	8-oz. glass	90
		354

PICKUP—Late afternoon		
Chilled orange juice	6-oz. glass	90

DINNER		
Dieter's Beef Stroganoff	1 serving	240
on rice	½ cup	90
Brussels sprouts	5	25
with chestnuts	1, sliced	20
Crisp celery	As desired	10
Fresh fruit cup	1 serving	85
Coffee, black		–
		470

Total calories for day: 1140

Calories

BREAKFAST

Chilled tangerine juice	4-oz. glass	55
Fried Egg—Slimming style	1	95
Toast	1 slice	60
Butter or margarine	½ pat	25
Coffee, black		–
		235

LUNCHEON

"Cream" of mushroom soup (skim milk)	1 bouillon cup	145
Tuna Fish Salad with Grapes	1 serving	120
Toasted Ry-Krisp	2 triple crackers	40
Hot tea		–
		305

PICKUP—Late afternoon

Tart apple	1 medium	70

DINNER

Fillet of flounder, baked	5 oz.	155
Lemon butter (1 tsp. butter, 1 tbsp. lemon juice)		40
Rice Pilaf	1 serving	150
Spinach	Large serving	30
Tomato Aspic Salad	1 mold	30
Melon balls, fresh or frozen	¾ cup	40
Coffee, black		–
		445

Total calories for day: 1055

Calories

BREAKFAST

Grapefruit	½ medium	60
Hot Wheatena	⅔ cup	100
Sugar	1 tsp.	16
Milk, whole	½ cup	80
Coffee, black		–
		256

LUNCHEON

Consommé with Sherry	1 bouillon cup	55
Grilled cheese sandwich		
Rye bread	1 slice	55
Cheese, process American	1-oz. slice	105
Canadian-style bacon	1 medium slice	55
Sliced tomatoes and chicory		35
Hot tea with lemon		–
		305

PICKUP—Late afternoon

Hot Cocoa (low-calorie)	1 cup	95

DINNER

Steak Kabobs	1 skewer	235
Baked potato	½ medium	45
Butter or margarine	½ pat	25
Romaine and chicory salad	1 serving	20
Gourmet Dressing	1½ tbsp.	24
Fresh Pineapple Deluxe	1 serving	95
Coffee, black		–
		444

Total calories for day: 1100

Calories

BREAKFAST

Orange-grapefruit juice	4-oz. glass	55
Shirred Egg	1	100
Toasted English muffin	½	70
Butter or margarine	½ pat	25
Coffee, black		–
		250

LUNCHEON

Skewer of Chicken Livers and Tomato	1 serving	150
Asparagus, with	6 spears	20
Parmesan cheese	1 tbsp., grated	20
Crisp celery hearts	As desired	10
Fresh pear	1	100
Hot tea with lemon		–
		300

PICKUP—Late afternoon

Skim milk or buttermilk	8-oz. glass	90

DINNER

Lamb Chop Stuffed with Mushrooms	1	250
Oven French Fries	1 serving	100
Broccoli	1 large stalk	25
Butter or margarine	½ pat	25
Beet and Onion Salad	1 serving	60
Sharp cheese	¾ oz.	85
Coffee, black		–
		545

Total calories for day: 1185

II

Adventures in
Low-Calorie Cooking

LOW-CALORIE COOKING

FAMILY weight control is largely up to the cook, for when overweight runs in families, fattening food habits invariably do too. At first blush you may feel that your flair for food counts two strikes against you. Get over that old-fashioned notion. With nutrition know-how and culinary ingenuity, you can serve delicious nonfattening meals.

In the recipes in this book the calories in each ingredient are listed. It is enormously helpful to know the calorie value of the various ingredients, and, incidentally, it is quite an eye opener. With this information, you can create other low-calorie dishes.

The calories have all been calculated with painstaking care. For your convenience in remembering, in most cases total calories are rounded to the nearest 5. The figuring has all been done for you. Just go ahead and prepare the dishes according to cooking instructions. If the size servings are limited to the amounts specified, you'll get slimming results.

In the recipes which follow, you will note that the calorie count of individual servings is given in round numbers. This process of rounding the values for easy remembering often affects the totals by 2 or 3 calories.

The seeming inconsistencies in calorie calculations of small amounts of an ingredient can be explained by what is known as "significant figures." Whole numbers are used, fractions are dropped.

In the interest of health as well as weight, in all your cooking use a minimum of fat. You will find that fats can be cut substantially in recipes without subtracting from the natural goodness of the dish. Whenever feasible, use unsaturated oil in place of solid, saturated fat. In cooking with oil, keep the flame very low.

In the menus and recipes, skim milk is specified. Skim milk can be purchased as such, or a large part of the fat can be removed from whole milk, provided it is not homogenized. Let the milk stand in the refrigerator for twenty-four hours in order to allow time for the fat to rise to the top. Then, before shaking, pour off two cups. The milk which remains in the bottom of the bottle is comparatively low in fat content. There is now on the market a new milk which contains only 2 percent butter fat, in contrast to the 3.7 percent content of regular whole milk.

In using nonfat dry milk, follow the directions in the recipes. As a beverage, prepare according to directions on package. For cereal, dilute with half the amount of water.

Go at low-calorie cooking in a spirit of adventure. You may turn out to be the best low-calorie cook in town. But more important, the health and happiness of your family are at stake. You can help your husband to add years to the best years of life. And your daughter need not be an overweight wallflower. Make weight control a family project. You, as chief cook, can help work a happy miracle.

If you are short and bordering on buxom, you get more miles to the calories, so to speak. For you these calorie-counted recipes will be a figure saver. Indeed, they can be a lifesaving measure.

Chapter 6

SAVORY SOUPS

HOT SOUP, consommé, and broth give soothing comfort for comparatively few calories, take the edge off a voracious appetite, and help the dieter to relax and enjoy the meal. Soup made with skim milk is an excellent way to incorporate milk into the menu.

To keep calories at a minimum, all visible fat should be skimmed off canned soups as well as homemade varieties.

Soups may be garnished with minced parsley, chives, or watercress, radish slices, a thin slice of lemon or orange, or thinly sliced unpeeled cucumber. To bland "creamed" soups, a little grated orange or lemon rind adds zip. Toasted chopped almonds give a gourmet touch.

One bouillon cup or soup dish holds 6 ounces, which is ¾ of a measuring cup.

Soups

CLAM CHOWDER—MANHATTAN

(Individual serving: 1 cup, large; 65 calories)

		Calories
Bacon	½ thin slice	15
Onion, diced	1 medium	20
Boiling water	1 qt.	–
Celery, diced	1 cup	17
Green pepper, diced	2 tbsp.	4
Carrots, raw, diced	1 cup	58
Potatoes, raw, diced	½ cup	62
Tomato juice	2 cups	90
Salt	1½ tsp.	–
Pepper	⅛ tsp.	–
Cayenne	Dash	–
Thyme, dried (optional)	Pinch	–
Clams, canned, minced	7½-oz. can, with liquid	110
	6 servings	376

Cut bacon into small pieces with scissors; cook with the onion about 5 minutes. Add boiling water, salt, celery, green pepper, and carrots. Simmer, covered, about 15 minutes. Add potatoes, tomato juice, and the rest of the seasonings. Simmer until potatoes are tender, about 20 minutes. Add clams with liquid; simmer, uncovered, 10 minutes. Test for seasoning.

CONSOMMÉ WITH SHERRY

(Individual serving: 1 bouillon cup; 55 calories)

		Calories
Beef Consommé, condensed	10½-oz. can	85
Bay leaf	1	–
Water	½ can	–
Sherry (cooking)	¼ cup (2 oz.)	80
	3 servings	165

Add water and bay leaf to beef consommé; simmer 5 minutes; remove bay leaf. Add cooking sherry; serve hot. Makes ⅔ cup each serving.

SAVORY OYSTER STEW

(Individual serving: 1 cup; 185 calories)

		Calories
Onion, chopped	1 medium	20
Carrot, chopped	1, 5½×1″	20
Celery, with leaves	2 large stalks	14
Butter or margarine	1 tbsp.	100
Bay leaf	Tip	–
Salt	1½ tsp.	–
Pepper	Dash	–
Milk	1 qt.	644
Oysters	1 pt.	320
	6 servings	1118

Chop vegetables; cook in the butter for a few minutes, stirring to prevent burning. Add tip of bay leaf and seasonings. Add milk; bring to boiling point, but *do not boil*. Meanwhile, have oysters in a pan, heating slowly; *do not cook them*. Strain hot milk mixture into oysters. Serve at once. This stew is so delicious you may want 1½ cups, for a calorie count of 285.

TOMATO BOUILLON

(Individual serving: 1 bouillon cup; 35 calories)

In saucepan combine 2 cups tomato juice, 1 bay leaf, 2 peppercorns, a stalk of diced celery, an onion slice, and salt to taste. Heat to the boiling point; simmer 10 minutes. Strain. Reheat and serve. Float a thin slice of lemon on each serving. Make 3 servings, ⅔ cup each.

HEARTY VEGETABLE SOUP

(Individual serving: 1 cup; 95 calories)

		Calories
Beef chuck	1 lb. (raw weight) (cooked value)	602
Water	3½ cups	–
Salt	1 tsp.	–
Pepper	To taste	–
Onion, diced	¾ cup	45
Celery, diced	⅔ cup	11
Potatoes, raw, diced	½ cup	62
Carrots, diced	¾ cup	43
Tomatoes, canned	2 cans 1-lb. each	190
	10 *cups*	953

Add water and seasonings to the beef chuck, which has been fat-trimmed and cut into small pieces; simmer until meat is tender, about 1½ hours. Add the prepared vegetables; cook until they are tender, about 25 minutes.

Chapter 7

THE MEAT OF THE MENU

PROTEIN FOODS are the backbone of slimming fare. Except for food fat, meat has the greatest satiety value of any food.

In this calorie-conscious age, weight watchers trim away the fat part of the meat and therefore should not be "charged" for the calories they do not eat. In some calorie charts now in use the values are based on untrimmed meats and include the fat with the lean.

In the calorie section in the back of the book two sets of values are included, those for very lean portions of meat and for lean and fat portions. These values, for the most part, are from the revised Handbook 8, of the United States Department of Agriculture. The lean values refer to very lean meat with no visible fat infiltration. The lean and fat portions contain the inseparable intermuscular fat. The fat rim was removed to within approximately one-half inch of the lean. Deposits of fat within the cut were not removed.

In the meat recipes the calorie count is based on the value of cooked lean meat. The amount of meat to order for the recipes is given in raw weight. The calorie value is on the yield of cooked meat from the amount of raw weight specified. This allows for shrinkage in cooking.

If lean cuts of meat are purchased and cooked in a way which eliminates as much fat as possible, then the calorie values for very lean meat hold true.

A small scale graduated in ounces and grams takes all the guesswork out of serving sizes and is an invaluable aid to dieters.

Meats

PAN-BROILED CUBE STEAKS

*(Individual serving: 1 steak, 4×4×⅜",
3½ oz., cooked—210 calories)*

Have steaks at room temperature. Heat a heavy skillet
piping hot; add just enough fat to keep the meat from sticking,
not more than ½ teaspoon. Pan-broil the steaks, allowing
1 minute for each side for thin steaks; thicker steaks will require 2 minutes for each side. Do not overcook. Season steaks
with salt and pepper; remove to a hot platter. If desired, add a
little water to the pan drippings; stir and heat until hot;
spoon over the steaks.

An alternative method is to omit fat; sprinkle the heated
skillet lightly with salt, and cook the steaks quickly as above.

Each cooked steak may be served on a *thin* slice of toasted
bread, for 45 additional calories.

BROILED SIRLOIN STEAK

*(Individual serving: ¼-lb. piece, 4×2×1",
lean meat only—235 calories)*

Choose a steak at least ¾ of an inch thick. Bring to room
temperature before broiling. Turn regulator of range to "broil"

and fully preheat broiler. Trim excess fat from the steak and slash fat edges in several places to prevent curling. Place steak on rack; place under heat unit so that top of meat is from 3 inches to 3½ inches under heat. Follow directions of range manufacturer as to whether door to broiling unit should be left partially open during the broiling process.

Broil top side for half the required broiling time; season the cooked side. Turn steak once, using a wide or spreading spatula, never a fork. Broil the other side for the rest of the required time.

TIME REQUIRED TO BROIL STEAK

Thickness	Rare	Medium
¾ to 1″	8 to 10 min.	12 to 14 min.
1½″	14 to 16 min.	18 to 20 min.
2″	35 to 40 min.	45 to 50 min.

Season second side of steak, if desired; remove to a hot platter and serve at once.

STEAK KABOBS

(*Individual serving: 1 kabob; 235 calories*)

		Calories
Sirloin steak (lean)	1¼ lbs.	880
	(raw weight)	
	(cooked value)	
Onion, sliced	1 medium	20
Mushrooms, canned whole	⅓ cup	19
Green pepper	1 medium	15
Salt	To season	–
Pepper	To season	–
	4 servings	934

Preheat broiler 10 minutes. Cut fat-trimmed meat into 12 chunks. Thinly slice onion. Drain mushrooms. Cut green pepper into small pieces. Arrange steak, onion slices, mushrooms, and green pepper alternately on 4 skewers. Place skewers across a shallow pan; broil 10 to 15 minutes, until well browned. Turn occasionally. Season with salt and pepper and serve immediately. Fresh mushrooms (½ pound—62 calories) may be used in place of the canned mushrooms.

PAN-BROILED GROUND BEEF

(Individual serving: 3-oz. patty; 160 calories)

Purchase 1 pound round steak. Have butcher trim fat from meat before grinding. Mix the lean beef with ¾ teaspoon of salt, ¼ teaspoon pepper, and a dash of Ac'cent, if desired. Form into 4 patties. Heat heavy iron skillet. Sprinkle skillet with salt in place of fat. Pan-broil patties to desired degree of doneness. Turn once during cooking. Patties may be cooked under broiler, if desired.

In recipes using ground round steak, the calorie count is based on lean beef. If hamburger is used, the calorie count is 185.

BEEF PATTIES BURGUNDY

(Individual serving: 1 patty; 180 calories)

		Calories
Ground beef (lean round steak)	1¼ lbs. (raw weight) (cooked value)	805
Mushrooms, canned, sliced	⅓ cup	19
Burgundy wine (cooking)	2 tbsp. (1 oz.)	30
Water chestnuts, thinly sliced, drained (optional)	½ of 5-oz. can	34
	5 servings	888

Form ground lean beef into 5 patties. In heated nonstick skillet (no fat), pan-broil patties to sear in juices. Add drained mushrooms and the Burgundy wine. Simmer slowly for 15 minutes. To add an elegant touch, just before removing from heat, add the thinly sliced water chestnuts.

BEEF POT ROAST

(Individual serving: 3 oz. meat; ½ potato; 1 carrot; ¼ cup onion; 2 tbsp. gravy—300 calories)

		Calories
Beef chuck	4 lbs. (raw weight) (cooked value)	2410
Fat (from meat)	1 tbsp.	125
Salt	1½ tsp.	–
Pepper	⅛ tsp.	–
Bay leaf	1 small	–
Water	½ cup	–
Onions, sliced	2 medium	40
Carrots, halved	4, 5½×1″	80
Potatoes, halved	4 medium, 2½″ diameter	372
		3027

Trim fat from meat; melt 1 tablespoon of fat (or drippings) in a heavy, covered kettle. Brown meat slowly on all sides in the fat. When browned, season meat with salt and pepper. Place a low rack under the meat; add the bay leaf, water, and the sliced onions. Cover tightly; cook slowly for 3 to 3½ hours, or until meat is tender. Add more water only if necessary. About 45 minutes before meat is done add the prepared vegetables. Remove meat and vegetables to a hot platter; keep hot while making gravy.

BROWN GRAVY

To make gravy acceptable for dieters, the fat should first be removed. A good plan is to pour off part of the liquid when roast is three-quarters done. Refrigerate this liquid in order that fat can congeal on top and be removed. By this method the fat-free gravy can be ready when the meat is cooked.

To make gravy from drippings and broth: Remove meat to platter and keep warm. (Pour off liquid remaining in pan, refrigerate for making more gravy at another time. Again, of course, the congealed fat on top must be removed.)

Remove fat from the drippings previously refrigerated, and reheat liquid. Add hot water or stock to make the desired amount of gravy, being sure that the brown drippings adhering to cooking pan are utilized. Two cups of liquid will make from 1½ to 2 cups of gravy. Use 1½ tablespoons of flour for each cup of gravy desired. Browned flour may be used to improve flavor. (To brown flour, heat it in a shallow pan over very low heat, stirring until slightly browned.)

Mix flour with a small amount of cold water; add slowly to liquid in pan; cook, stirring constantly, until thickened and smooth. Season to taste. If desired, a bit of Kitchen Bouquet may be added to improve color and flavor of gravy.

OVENBURGERS

(Individual serving: 1 ovenburger; 165 calories)

		Calories
Onion, chopped	2 tbsp.	8
Ground beef, lean round	1¼ lbs.	805
	(raw weight)	
	(cooked value)	
Bread crumbs, soft	½ cup	60
	(1 slice bread)	
Catsup	2 tbsp.	40
Salt	1 tsp.	–
Pepper	Dash	–
Worcestershire sauce	½ tsp.	2
Egg	1 medium	80
	6 servings	995

Preheat oven to 350°. Chop onion; combine with ground beef, bread crumbs, and seasonings. Add egg and blend well. Form into 6 round cakes; place in a shallow oven platter or baking dish. Bake from 20 to 25 minutes.

Variations: Vary seasonings to taste. Horseradish or prepared mustard may be used in place of the onion. A few tablespoons of pickle relish may be added. Or the ovenburgers could be baked plain (using crumbs and egg) and a barbecue sauce served over them.

OVEN CROQUETTES

(Individual serving: 2 croquettes; 165 calories)

		Calories
Meat, cooked, ground (lean meat only)	2 cups	435
Butter or margarine	1 tsp.	35
Flour	1 tbsp.	25
Salt	To taste	–
Pepper	Dash	–
Parsley, chopped	1 tbsp.	1
Bouillon (from beef cube)	½ cup	2
Skim milk	½ cup	45
Onion, raw, chopped	2 tbsp.	8
Green pepper, chopped	2 tbsp.	4
Egg	1 medium	80
Worcestershire sauce	1 tsp.	4
Chili sauce	1 tbsp.	20
	4 servings	659

Trim all visible fat from cooked meat; put lean meat through grinder. Melt butter; add flour and seasonings; blend well. Add bouillon and skim milk; stir and cook until slightly thickened. Add ground meat, chopped vegetables, egg, Worcestershire sauce, and chili sauce. Blend well and heat through. Preheat oven to 375°. Use a small mold to form mixture into 8 croquettes. Place them on a lightly greased oven platter or glass piepan. Bake for about 25 minutes.

MUSHROOM MEAT LOAF

(Center slice, 4×2½×¾", 3½ oz.; 160 calories)

		Calories
Mushrooms, fresh, sliced	½ cup	10
Onion, minced	2 tbsp.	8
Green pepper, chopped	2 tbsp.	4
Celery, chopped	½ cup	8
Bread crumbs, soft	½ cup	60
	(1 slice bread)	
Egg, beaten	1 medium	80
Milk	¼ cup	40
Catsup	1 tbsp.	20
Worcestershire sauce	1 tbsp.	12
Salt	1½ to 2 tsp.	–
Pepper	¼ tsp.	–
Ground beef	2 lbs. (raw weight)	1205
(lean chuck)	(cooked value)	
	2-lb. loaf	1447

Preheat oven to 400°. Chop vegetables with the bread. In a small bowl beat egg; add milk, catsup, Worcestershire sauce, and seasonings. Combine mixtures with the ground chuck; blend well. Form into a loaf; place on rack in baking pan with cover. Pour ½ cup hot water into pan; cover and bake 1 hour. Remove cover the last 15 minutes of baking to brown top of loaf. If desired, loaf may be baked in an oven-glass bread pan. Omit the water. Cover loaf with aluminum foil the first 45 minutes. On removing from oven, drain off all drippings. Serve hot or cold. Luncheon-size slice: 4×2½×½" (3 oz.), 135 calories.

BARBECUED FRANKFURTER KABOBS

(*Individual serving: 1 kabob; 260 calories*)

		Calories
Frankfurters, quartered	4, 5½" long	620
Onions, sliced	4 medium	80
Tomatoes, quartered	2 medium, 2×2½"	70
Mushrooms, raw, whole	8 large	56
Barbecue sauce:		
Butter or margarine	1½ tsp.	50
Green pepper, chopped	¼ cup	9
Onion, chopped	1 small	10
Chili sauce	½ cup	142
Tabasco	1 drop	–
Salt	½ tsp.	–
Pepper	Dash	–
	4 servings	1037

Preheat oven 10 minutes at 350°. To make barbecue sauce: melt butter in a small skillet; cook the chopped green pepper and onion for about 3 minutes; add chili sauce and seasonings. Simmer about 8 minutes. Put frankfurters in hot water for a moment or two; drain; dry. Prepare kabobs by arranging alternately on 4 skewers pieces of the quartered frankfurters, onion slices, tomato wedges, and mushrooms. Broil under medium heat until lightly browned, turning meanwhile. Spread with half the sauce; broil 5 minutes; turn; spread with the rest of the sauce; broil 5 minutes longer. To catch the drippings place a pan beneath the skewers or line the broiler with foil.

STUFFED GREEN PEPPERS

(Individual serving: 2 half peppers; 250 calories)

		Calories
Green peppers	4 medium	60
Corned beef hash, canned	1-lb. can	820
Onion, chopped	1 tbsp.	4
Tomato purée, canned	¼ cup	24
Bread crumbs, soft	½ slice bread	30
Butter or margarine	2 tsp.	68
Parsley (optional)		–
	4 servings	1006

Wash the peppers; cut out stem ends; cut in half lengthwise. Parboil the peppers about 5 minutes; drain. Heat oven to 350°. Combine the canned corned beef hash with the chopped onion; blend in the tomato purée. Stuff the pepper halves; top with the bread crumbs and dot each half pepper with ¼ teaspoon butter. Place them in a shallow glass baking pan; pour a little hot water around them; bake about 25 minutes. Serve on a heated platter, garnished with parsley.

SPICED VEAL CUTLET

(Individual serving: 3 oz.; 230 calories)

		Calories
Veal cutlet	1 lb. (raw weight) (cooked value)	735
Garlic clove, cut (optional)	1	3
Flour	1 tbsp.	25
Seasoned salt	1 tsp.	–

		Calories
Herbs, crushed (sage, thyme, basil)	Pinch	–
Salad oil	1 tbsp.	125
Hot water	½ cup	–
Worcestershire sauce	1 tsp.	4
Lemon slices	1 lemon	20
	4 servings	912

Rub surface of meat with cut garlic clove. Mix flour, seasoned salt, and just a pinch of desired herbs, crushed. Sprinkle meat on both sides with the mixture. Heat salad oil in skillet; brown meat slowly on both sides; watch carefully that it does not burn. Add hot water and Worcestershire sauce. Simmer, covered, until tender—about 45 minutes. Serve with lemon slices.

SKEWERED LAMB AND PINEAPPLE

(Individual serving: 1 skewer; 180 calories)

		Calories
Lamb leg, lean	1 lb. (raw weight) (cooked value)	525
Salad oil	½ tbsp.	60
Vinegar (or lemon juice)	¼ cup vinegar	8
Meat tenderizer	½ tsp.	–
Seasonings (salt, pepper, garlic salt)	To season	–
Ac'cent	Dash	–
Herbs (marjoram, basil, rosemary)	Pinch	–
Pineapple chunks, canned, drained	24 medium	125
	4 servings	718

Cut lean lamb into 24 1-inch cubes. Place in dish; sprinkle with the combined salad oil, vinegar, and meat tenderizer.

Turn pieces to coat all sides. Combine seasonings and crushed herbs; sprinkle over meat. Refrigerate at least 3 hours. Preheat broiler. Drain canned pineapple. Arrange alternate cubes of lamb and pineapple on 4 skewers. Place on broiler rack about 2 inches below heat. Broil until meat is brown, about 20 minutes, turning to brown all sides.

VEAL SCALOPPINE

(Individual serving: 3 oz.; 230 calories)

		Calories
Veal cutlet, thinly cut for scaloppine	1 lb. (raw weight) (cooked value)	735
Flour	1 tbsp.	25
Salad oil	1 tbsp.	125
Garlic powder (optional)	½ tsp.	–
Nutmeg	¼ tsp.	–
Instant minced onion flakes, canned	1 tsp.	7
Salt	To taste	–
Pepper	To taste	–
Mushrooms, canned, sliced	3-oz. can, with liquid	28
Green pepper, chopped	2 tbsp.	4
Lemon juice	1 tbsp.	4
Water	¾ cup	–
	4 servings	928

Dredge veal with flour. Brown slowly on both sides in the hot oil. Add remaining ingredients, including liquid with mushrooms. Cover and simmer 15 minutes, or until veal is tender.

LAMB CHOPS STUFFED WITH MUSHROOMS

(*Individual serving: 1 chop; 250 calories*)

		Calories
Lamb chops, cut double-thick	4 chops, 1½″ thick	840
Mushrooms, fresh	½ lb.	62
Butter	1 tbsp.	100
	4 servings	1002

Cut a deep pocket in meaty side of chops. Chop mushrooms fine (caps and stems) and sauté in the butter. Cool. Stuff into pockets of lamb chops. Use toothpicks to hold together. Season chops. Broil.

DIETER'S BEEF STROGANOFF

(*Individual serving: ½ cup, large; 240 calories*)

		Calories
Beef tenderloin	1 lb. (raw weight) (cooked value)	760
Butter or margarine	2 tbsp.	200
Mushrooms, fresh, sliced	½ lb.	62
Onion, chopped	½ cup	30
Beef bouillon, canned, condensed	10½-oz. can	65
Buttermilk	½ cup	45
Flour	2 tbsp.	50
Salt	To taste	–
Pepper	To taste	–
	5 servings	1212

Have trimmed beef tenderloin sliced ¼ inch thick. Cut into strips ¼ inch wide. Brown quickly in butter in skillet. Push meat to one side; add sliced fresh mushrooms (about 3 cups) and chopped onion. Cook till tender, but not brown. Add condensed beef bouillon; heat just to boiling. Blend buttermilk with flour; stir into bouillon. Cook, stirring constantly, till thickened (sauce will be thin). Add salt and pepper. May be served over hot rice. Makes 3 cups.

CHINESE POT ROAST

(Individual serving: ¼ lb.; 240 calories)

		Calories
Salad oil	2 tbsp.	250
Ginger root, fresh or dry, grated	1 tsp.	–
Beef chuck	3 lbs. (raw weight) (cooked value)	1805
Dry sherry	2 tbsp.	40
Soy sauce	3 tbsp.	30
Water	¼ cup	–
Anise seed, crushed	3 seeds	–
Green onions, with stalks	3 stalks	25
Salt	1 tsp.	–
	9 servings	2150

Place the salad oil and the ginger in preheated pot. When oil is hot, brown meat well on all sides. Pour off fat; add the dry sherry and soy sauce. Cook five minutes. Add water, the crushed anise seed, and the green onion stalks. Cover the pot and cook over low heat until tender—about 3 hours. While cooking turn meat several times, adding a little water as needed. Season with salt in the last hour of cooking.

SUKIYAKI

(Individual serving: ⅔ cup; 220 calories)

		Calories
Fillet of beef or boneless sirloin	1 lb. (raw weight) (cooked value)	760
Soy sauce	¼ cup	40
Sugar	1 tbsp.	48
Beef broth	½ cup	15
Sherry	1 tbsp.	20
Onions, thinly sliced	1 cup	60
Celery, sliced	1 cup	17
Bamboo shoots, sliced	1 cup	36
Mushrooms, fresh, thinly sliced	½ lb.	62
Scallions (green onions), cut in pieces	4, with tops	30
Salad oil	2 tbsp.	250
	6 *servings*	1338

Have meat fat-trimmed and cut in ⅛-inch slices. Combine soy sauce, sugar, beef broth, and sherry. Prepare vegetables. Heat oil in heavy skillet. Brown meat strips and push to side of skillet. Pour half of soy mixture over meat. Add celery and onions; cook 3 minutes. Add remaining ingredients and remaining soy-sauce mixture. Cook 4 minutes. Serve immediately, with rice.

Sukiyaki is an interesting dish to cook at the table in an electric skillet, at 350°.

Poultry

CHICKEN PAPRIKA

(Individual serving: ¼ of 2-lb. broiler; 190 calories)

Preheat oven at 375° for fully 20 minutes. Wash and dry cut-up chicken. Place pieces in baking pan, skin side up. Sprinkle chicken with juice of half lemon, salt, pepper, and paprika. Bake, uncovered, 30 to 45 minutes. For the last 5 minutes increase heat to 450°.

SKEWER OF CHICKEN LIVERS AND TOMATO

(Individual serving: 150 calories)

		Calories
Chicken livers	3 (3 oz.)	110
Salt	Sprinkle	–
Flour	½ tsp.	4
Tomato	1 small	25
Butter	¼ tsp.	10
		149

Wash chicken livers, salt lightly, sift on thin sprinkle of flour. Wash tomato and quarter. Arrange on skewer, alternating chicken liver with tomato quarter. Add dab of butter. Place skewer in shallow pan. Preheat oven 10 minutes at 400°. Bake for 20 minutes.

GOLDEN-BROWN CHICKEN—SLIMMING STYLE

(*Individual serving:* ½ *lb.;* 215 *calories*)

		Calories
Chicken, disjointed	2½-lb. chicken	955
Salad oil	2 tsp.	80
Salt	1 tsp.	–
Pepper	¼ tsp.	–
Ac'cent	As desired	–
Flour	2 tbsp.	50
	5 *servings*	1085

Preheat oven at 400° for fully 20 minutes. Wash and dry chicken. Place pieces in a shallow pan, skin side up. Brush each piece lightly with the salad oil. Combine seasonings, Ac'cent, and flour; sift evenly over chicken. Pour ½ cup hot water into pan (more later, if needed). Bake, uncovered, until brown. Reduce heat to 300° and continue baking, uncovered, until chicken is tender. Total cooking time about 1 hour. After the first 30 minutes, baste chicken; baste once or twice again during cooking.

BROILED CHICKEN

(*Individual serving:* ¼ *of* 2-*lb. broiler;* 190 *calories*)

Delicious broiled chicken can be prepared without the addition of fat. The secret lies in cooking it quickly to seal in juices. Preheat broiler 10 minutes. Arrange split, cleaned broiler halves skin side down on broiler. If desired, first line broiler pan with aluminum foil. Have chicken 4 to 6 inches from the heat. Broil 15 minutes; sprinkle with salt; turn over. Broil skin side up for 15 minutes—basting not necessary. Season with salt and pepper. Serve at once.

BAKED CHICKEN LIVERS

(Individual serving: 3 chicken livers; 125 calories)

		Calories
Chicken livers	9 (9 oz.)	330
Seasoning	Sprinkle	–
Flour	1 tsp.	8
Butter	1 tsp.	35
	3 *servings*	373

Wash chicken livers, season. Sift over light sprinkling of flour; dot with butter. Place in a shallow pan. Preheat oven at 400° for 10 minutes. Bake chicken livers for 25 minutes.

Fish and Shellfish

DEVILED CRABMEAT IN GREEN PEPPERS

(Individual serving: 1 pepper; 180 calories)

		Calories
Green peppers	3 medium	45
Butter or margarine	½ tbsp.	50
Onion, minced	1 tbsp.	4
Bread crumbs, soft	1 cup	120
	(2 slices bread)	
Salt	¼ tsp.	–
Cayenne	Few grains	–
Mustard, prepared	Dash	–
Egg yolk, beaten	1 yolk	60
Skim milk	½ cup	45
Crabmeat, canned, flaked	1 cup	170
Cheese, Parmesan, grated	2 tbsp.	40
	3 servings	534

Wash green peppers; cut a thin slice from the top of each pepper and remove seeds. Simmer peppers in boiling salted water from 7 to 10 minutes or until almost tender; drain. Melt butter in saucepan; add minced onion; cook 2 minutes; add bread crumbs and seasonings. In a small bowl beat egg yolk; add skim milk slowly, blending well. Add flaked crab-meat and egg-yolk mixture to saucepan mixture. When well blended and hot throughout, fill the green peppers. Top each with grated cheese; place on heat-proof dish and set in broiler pan. Broil in preheated broiler until cheese is melted and lightly browned. The deviled crabmeat may be baked on scallop shells. In this case, 2 tablespoons of minced green pepper should be cooked in the butter with the onion.

CRABMEAT RAMEKINS

(Individual serving: ⅔ cup; 165 calories)

		Calories
Skim milk	⅓ cup	30
Cream of celery soup, condensed, undiluted	10½-oz. can	240
Mushrooms, canned, drained	⅔ cup	37
Crabmeat, canned, flaked	1 cup	170
Lemon juice	2 tsp.	3
Bread, soft, cubed	½ cup (1 slice)	60
Cheese, American, grated	¼ cup	112
	4 servings	652

Add skim milk to condensed cream of celery soup; heat slowly. Add drained mushrooms, crabmeat, lemon juice, and the cubed bread. Turn into 4 lightly greased ramekins. Top each with 1 tablespoon of the grated cheese. Bake at 350° until heated through.

CREOLE HALIBUT FILLETS

(Individual serving: ⅓ lb., with sauce; 165 calories)

		Calories
Creole Sauce	2 cups	228
Halibut fillets	2 lbs. (raw weight) (cooked value)	775
Salt	To season	–
Pepper	To season	–
	6 servings	1003

Make Creole Sauce. Preheat oven to 400°. Arrange halibut fillets in a lightly greased baking pan or bake-and-serve platter. Sprinkle lightly with salt and pepper. Pour Creole Sauce over fish. Bake, uncovered, from 30 to 45 minutes, until fish is tender. If frozen fish is used, partially defrost; it will require the longer baking period.

BROILED OCEAN PERCH FILLETS

(Individual serving: ⅓ lb., 190 calories)

		Calories
Ocean perch fillets, frozen	1 lb. (raw weight) (cooked value)	520
Butter or margarine, melted	½ tbsp.	50
Lemon juice	1 tbsp.	4
Salt	¼ to ½ tsp.	–
Pepper	Dash	–
Paprika	Dash	–
	3 servings	574

Thaw frozen fish just enough to separate fillets. Preheat broiler, using medium heat (350°). Arrange fillets, skin side down, on greased broiler pan or rack. A broil-and-serve platter may be used for the fish. Brush the fillets with the melted butter and lemon juice; sprinkle with salt, pepper, and paprika. Broil fish 2 to 3 inches from heat for 10 to 15 minutes, or until fish is easily flaked with a fork, but still moist. Baste fish several times. It is not necessary to turn fish fillets.

CRABMEAT MARYLAND

(*Individual serving: ½ cup; 180 calories*)

		Calories
Butter or margarine	2 tbsp.	200
Flour	2 tbsp.	50
Milk	1½ cups	240
Onion, minced	2 tbsp.	8
Celery salt	½ tsp.	–
Orange rind, grated	⅛ tsp.	–
Parsley, chopped	1 tbsp.	1
Green pepper, minced	2 tbsp.	4
Pimiento, minced	1 pimiento	10
Tabasco	Dash	–
Sherry (cooking)	2 tbsp.	40
Egg, beaten	1 medium	80
Salt	¾ to 1 tsp.	–
Pepper	Speck	–
Crabmeat, flaked	2 cups	340
Bread crumbs, soft	½ cup	60
	(1 slice bread)	
Butter, melted	½ tbsp.	50
Paprika	Dash	–
	6 *servings*	1083

Melt 2 tablespoons butter in double boiler; stir in flour and milk; cook, stirring, until thickened. Add onion, celery salt, orange rind, parsley, green pepper, pimiento, and tabasco. Remove from heat; add sherry. Stir some of sauce slowly into beaten egg; stir egg mixture into rest of sauce. Add salt, pepper, and crabmeat; turn into greased casserole. Mix bread crumbs with ½ tablespoon melted butter and paprika; sprinkle over top of crabmeat. Bake, uncovered, in 350° oven 15 to 20 minutes, or until brown.

Eggs

SCRAMBLED EGGS

(Individual serving: ½ cup, large; 170 calories)

		Calories
Eggs	4 medium	320
Skim milk	¼ cup	22
Salt	¼ tsp.	–
Pepper	Speck	–
Herbs (optional)	Pinch	–
	2 *servings*	342

Have water boiling in the bottom part of a double boiler; let
the top part of the boiler become heated over the water while
preparing the eggs. Break eggs into a small bowl; beat with
rotary beater. Add the skim milk and season to taste. A dash
of herb—orégano or marjoram—may be added. Some like a bit
of curry. Pour the mixture into the heated double-boiler top;
cover and let eggs cook over the boiling water until of the
desired consistency. A teflon-lined pan may be used in place
of double boiler. Stir occasionally (but not continuously) with
a wooden spoon. Remove the eggs from heat before they are
quite done, as they will continue to cook in the heated cooker.

Serve as soon as possible after removal from heat. For a gourmet touch, add toasted sesame seeds, about a teaspoon.

Variation: To lower fat content, use 3 eggs and 1 additional egg white. Proceed as above. Individual serving: 140 calories.

BAKED (or Shirred) EGG

(Individual serving: 1 egg; 100 calories)

		Calories
Milk	1 tbsp.	10
Egg	1 medium	80
Salt	To taste	–
Pepper	To taste	–
Butter or margarine	¼ tsp.	10
Paprika	Sprinkle	–
		100

Preheat oven to 325°. Lightly butter a shallow individual baking dish. Place the milk in the bottom of the dish; break the egg into it. (Some prefer to pour the milk over the egg.) Season to taste with salt and pepper. Dot with the butter. Bake, uncovered, until egg is set, from 15 to 20 minutes. Garnish with paprika.

FRIED EGG—SLIMMING STYLE

(Individual serving: 95 calories)

		Calories
Butter or margarine	½ tsp.	17
Egg	1 medium	80
Salt	To taste	–
Pepper	To taste	–
		97

Use a small, heavy iron skillet or teflon-lined pan; heat the butter; be sure that bottom of skillet is coated with the fat. Add egg and cook over *low heat* until of the desired degree of doneness, from 3 to 4 minutes. Cover the skillet so that egg will cook on top without additional fat. Sprinkle with salt and pepper or with seasoned salt.

Variation: For the ½ teaspoon butter in recipe, substitute ½ teaspoon salad oil (20 calories). Heat oil in skillet over *very low flame*. Put in egg and start cooking; add 1 scant tablespoon hot water. Cover. Cook until done. Calorie value: 100.

FRENCH OMELET

(Individual serving: 230 calories)

		Calories
Eggs	2 medium	160
Water	2 tbsp.	–
Salt	¼ tsp., scant	–
Pepper	Few grains	–
Butter	2 tsp.	68
Parsley		–
		228

Break eggs into a soup plate. Beat slightly with a fork; add water and continue beating only until yolks and whites are blended. Season. Melt the butter slowly in an 8-inch skillet; make sure that it is coated with the butter. Pour in egg mixture; cook slowly, lifting omelet as it cooks and tipping skillet so that uncooked mixture flows underneath cooked portion. With spatula, form into a roll, with softer portion inside. Slip onto a heated platter; garnish with parsley.

DEVILED EGGS

(Individual serving: 1 egg; 85 calories)

		Calories
Eggs, hard-cooked	6 medium	480
Celery, minced	1 tsp.	–
Onion, minced (optional)	1 tsp.	1
Salt	¼ to ½ tsp.	–
Pepper	Dash	–
Paprika	Dash	–
Dry mustard	¼ to ½ tsp.	–
Parsley, minced	1 tsp.	–
Cooked Salad Dressing	2 tbsp.	30
	6 servings	511

Halve hard-cooked eggs lengthwise. Remove yolks, mash with the minced vegetables, seasonings, and Cooked Salad Dressing. Refill egg whites, heaping filling slightly. Vary filling to suit taste. A bit of chopped sweet pickle, horseradish, a few drops of Worcestershire sauce, or ¼ teaspoon curry powder may be used.

FLUFFY OMELET

(Individual serving: ½ omelet; 155 calories)

		Calories
Eggs, separated	3 medium	240
Water	3 tbsp.	–
Salt	½ tsp., scant	–
Pepper	Few grains	–
Butter or margarine	2 tsp.	68
Parsley		–
	2 servings	308

Preheat oven to 325°. Beat egg whites until stiff; set aside. With same beater, beat egg yolks well; add water and seasonings. Fold yolk mixture into stiffly beaten whites. Melt the butter in a skillet with heat-proof handle; pour in egg mixture. Cook over low heat about 3 minutes. When puffy and browned on the bottom, finish cooking in oven, about 10 minutes longer. Crease through the center, fold one half over the other; slip onto hot platter. Garnish with parsley sprigs.

OMELET WITH *FINES HERBES*

(Individual serving: 200 calories)

		Calories
Salad oil (or butter)	1 tsp. oil	40
Eggs	2 medium	160
Water	2 tbsp.	–
Herbs (chives, parsley, chervil, tarragon)	½ tsp. (or less)	–
Salt	¼ tsp.	–
Pepper	Speck	–
		200

Heat oil (or butter) in 8-inch skillet, over low heat. Beat eggs with the water; add herbs and seasonings. Prepare as in French Omelet. Serve on heated serving plate.

Note: If the herbs used are dried, use half as much as if fresh.

POACHED EGG SUPREME

(Individual serving: 205 calories)

		Calories
Canadian-style bacon, grilled	1 medium slice, 3″ diameter × ⅛″	55
Egg, poached	1 medium	80
English muffin, toasted	½	70
		205

Grill slice of Canadian bacon; drain on absorbent paper. Poach egg and toast ½ English muffin. Place the bacon on the toasted muffin half. Top with the poached egg. Season to taste. Serve hot.

Chapter 8

FLAVORFUL VEGETABLES

VEGETABLES can add greatly to the joy of eating if they are cooked exactly right. In low-calorie fare, vegetables cannot be enhanced by rich sauces, so proper cooking and subtle seasoning are especially important.

In order to bring out their unique goodness vegetables should be cooked quickly in a minimum of water and removed from the fire during their tender, delicious stage. Overcooking is ruinous.

Some vegetables, such as green leaves, can be cooked primarily in their own juices, with just the water that clings to the washed leaves. In French cookery two or three dripping-wet lettuce leaves are often used in place of water. Moisture from the leaves is brought out by the heat. A heavy cooking utensil should be used. Regardless of the method of cooking, there should be little or no water remaining in the pan when the vegetable is done.

Common vegetables can be given an uncommon touch by the addition of herbs while cooking. *Use the light touch.* A good rule is to take as tiny a pinch as you think is needed, then cut that amount in half—it requires so *little* to give the desired subtle flavor.

Try these combinations for a magic flavor touch: Basil gives a lift to asparagus, carrots, green beans, and tomatoes. Dill is especially good with Brussels sprouts, cauliflower, green beans, fresh tomatoes, cabbage, and carrots. Marjoram is just right with carrots, spinach, and zucchini. A gourmet touch can be given mushrooms, string beans, and tomatoes with orégano—or try a bay leaf in tomatoes. Thyme is a favorite with asparagus, aspics, beets, and tomatoes. Favorite herbs to use with carrots are mint, ginger, and chives. With the squash family, nutmeg is a delightful spice to use.

Mild-flavored vegetables are improved by the use of monosodium glutamate (Ac'cent). Vegetables may be cooked in consommé, or a bouillon cube may be added to the cooking water.

For vegetables such as artichokes and broccoli, which cry out for butter in serving, use lemon juice in a small amount of melted butter to lessen calories and add flavor.

Vegetables

PANNED SUMMER SQUASH

(*Individual serving: ½ cup, large; 30 calories*)

Scrub a 1-pound summer squash; remove thin slice from stem and blossom ends, but do not pare or remove seeds if squash is young. Cut into pieces. Place in a heavy pan with a tightly fitting cover. Season squash lightly with salt and pepper. Simmer over *very low heat* until squash is tender—about 20 minutes. Do not add any water or fat. Stir squash off bottom of pan occasionally. Makes 3 servings.

BAKED TOMATOES

(*Individual serving: 2 halves; 45 calories*)

		Calories
Tomatoes	4 medium, 2×2½"	140
Onion, minced	1 small	10
Salt	To taste	–
Worcestershire sauce or minced basil	As desired	–
Butter or margarine	1 tsp.	35
	4 servings	185

Preheat oven to 375°. Wash tomatoes and remove stem ends; halve crosswise. Arrange on an oven platter or shallow baking dish, cut sides up. Sprinkle tops with the minced onion; season with salt; add a drop of Worcestershire sauce, or a bit of minced basil, if desired. Dot each half with ¼ teaspoon butter. Bake, uncovered, until tender, from 25 to 30 minutes. Garnish platter with parsley.

TOMATO SCALLOP

(*Individual serving: ½ cup; 40 calories*)

		Calories
Butter	1 tsp.	35
Onion, sliced	1 small	10
Green pepper, diced	1 medium	15
Celery, diced	2 medium stalks	10
Tomatoes, canned	1-lb. can	95
Salt	To taste	–
Pepper	Dash	–
Bay leaf or basil	As desired	–
Brown sugar	¼ tsp.	4
Bread crumbs, soft	½ cup (1 slice bread)	60
	6 servings	229

Preheat oven to 350°. Melt butter in a small skillet; cook the raw vegetables until tender. Put canned tomatoes in a casserole; break up the large pieces. Season with salt and pepper; add a tip of bay leaf or a pinch of basil if desired. Add the brown sugar and the vegetables. Crumble the bread into the skillet and stir about to absorb juice left from cooking the vegetables; add to tomato mixture. Bake until heated through, about 25 minutes.

BROILED TOMATOES

(Individual serving: 2 halves; 60 calories)

		Calories
Tomatoes	1 medium, 2×2½"	35
Salt	Sprinkle	–
Pepper	Dash	–
Onion juice	Few drops	–
Cheese, process American, grated	1 tbsp.	25
Parsley, chopped	1 tsp.	–
		60

Use 1 firm tomato for each person to be served. Peel or not, as desired. Halve tomatoes or cut them into thick slices crosswise. Arrange on a lightly greased shallow pan or heat-proof platter. Season to taste; sprinkle with the onion juice and grated cheese. Lay platter on broiler pan; broil from 3 to 5 minutes, at 350°. If dish used is breakable, make sure that it does not come into contact with flame. If not cooked through, finish cooking in oven. Add parsley just before serving.

BAKED JULIENNE BEETS

(Individual serving: ½ cup; 40 calories)

		Calories
Beets, canned (julienne style)	1-lb. can	154
Salt	To season	–
Pepper	To season	–
Lemon juice	2 tsp.	3
Sugar	½ tsp.	8
Beet liquor	3 tbsp.	–
	4 servings	165

Preheat oven to 350°. Drain beets; spread them evenly in a small glass casserole. Season with salt and pepper. Add the lemon juice. Sprinkle the sugar over beets; add about 3 tablespoons of the beet liquor. Cover; bake until beets are heated through, about 20 minutes.

SPICED BEETS

(*Individual serving: ⅓ cup; 30 calories*)

		Calories
Beets, canned	1-lb. can	154
Onion, chopped	1 tbsp.	4
Salt	½ tsp.	–
Cloves, ground	⅛ tsp.	–
Nutmeg	⅛ tsp.	–
Pepper	Dash	–
Sugar	1 tsp.	16
Beet liquor	¾ cup	–
Lemon juice	3 tbsp.	12
	6 servings	186

Drain canned beets; slice or dice. Add the chopped onion, salt, spices, pepper, and sugar to the beet liquor; heat to boiling. Add lemon juice and pour over the beets. Serve hot or cold.

OVEN FRENCH FRIES

(Individual serving: ½ cup; 100 calories)

		Calories
Potatoes, raw	3 medium	280
Salad oil	1 tbsp.	125
Water	1 tbsp.	–
Salt	To taste	–
	4 servings	405

Preheat oven at 425°. Cut raw potatoes into strips. Mix oil and water in bowl; add potato strips and mix until coated with mixture. Place in shallow pan. Bake 45 minutes to 1 hour at 425°. Salt lightly and serve hot. Raw potatoes may be prepared shoestring style.

CARROTS AND MUSHROOMS

(Individual serving: ½ cup; 35 calories)

Carrots, sliced	2 cups	115
Salt	½ tsp.	–
Pepper	Dash	–
Ginger	⅛ to ¼ tsp.	–
Mushrooms, canned, sliced	3-oz. can, with liquid	28
	4 servings	143

Slice carrots into saucepan; sprinkle with salt, pepper, and ginger. Add canned mushrooms, including the liquid (but not any added fat). Cover tightly; bring to boil. Cook gently until carrots are just tender, from 5 to 10 minutes. Serve immediately.

BAKED STUFFED ZUCCHINI

(*Individual serving: 1 squash; 40 calories*)

		Calories
Zucchini squash	4 small (1½ lbs.)	110
Onion, chopped	1 small	10
Salt	½ tsp. or to taste	–
Pepper	⅛ tsp.	–
Bread crumbs, soft	1 tbsp.	8
Salad oil or butter	1 tsp. oil	40
	4 servings	168

Scrub zucchini well; cut off ends; do not pare. Parboil whole squash in boiling water until tender but firm, about 15 minutes. Preheat oven to 400°. Cut shallow slice off top of squash; place in mixing bowl. Scoop out inside of squash and add pulp to that in the mixing bowl. Mix pulp with chopped onion and seasonings. Replace in squash shells; sprinkle with bread crumbs; add salad oil or butter. Bake for 30 minutes.

GREEN BEANS WITH MUSHROOMS AND PARMESAN CHEESE

(*Individual serving: ⅔ cup; 45 calories*)

		Calories
Green beans, frozen	10-oz. package	75
Salt	To taste	–
Pepper	To taste	–
Thyme (optional)	Pinch	–
Mushrooms, canned,	½ cup	28
Cheese, Parmesan, grated	4 tbsp.	80
	4 servings	183

Cook green beans according to package directions. Season with salt, pepper, and, if desired, thyme. Heat the canned mushrooms in their liquid; drain, add to cooked beans. Lift beans and mushrooms to a heated oven-proof platter; sprinkle with the grated Parmesan cheese and place under broiler flame until cheese is just melted.

RICE PILAF

(Individual serving: ½ cup; 150 calories)

		Calories
Rice, raw	1 cup	695
Salad oil	1 tbsp.	125
Consommé, beef	10½-oz. can	85
Water	⅔ cup (scant)	–
Cloves, whole	3	–
Onion (for seasoning)	1 small	–
Salt	¼ tsp.	–
	6 servings	905

Preheat oven to 375°. In skillet, brown rice in the oil. Dilute consommé with the water; heat to boiling point. Stick cloves in peeled onion. Combine browned rice, hot consommé, onion, and salt in casserole. Cover tightly. Bake, covered, for 25 minutes, or until rice is tender and liquid absorbed. Remove onion. Serve hot. May be pressed into a mold.

BAKED ACORN SQUASH

(Individual serving: ½ squash; 75 calories)

		Calories
Acorn squash	2 medium	200
Butter or margarine, melted	1 tbsp.	100
Nutmeg	Dash	–
Salt	To season	–
Pepper	To season	–
	4 servings	300

Preheat oven to 400°. Scrub acorn squash. Cut in half lengthwise, scrape out seeds and stringy portion. Place *cut side down* in lightly greased baking pan. Bake for 45 minutes. Remove from oven. Brush inside of squash halves with melted butter; add seasonings. Return to oven and bake 15 minutes longer.

Other herbs that may be used are Season-All and basil leaves. For a gourmet touch, add 2 slivered filberts for the last 15 minutes of baking.

ASPARAGUS WITH MUSHROOMS

(Individual serving: 65 calories)

		Calories
Asparagus, fresh (or 10-oz. pkg., frozen)	1 lb.	66
Butter or margarine	1 tbsp.	100
Mushrooms, canned, sliced	3-oz. can, with liquid	28
	3 servings	194

Use heavy skillet. Cut asparagus on the diagonal. Heat butter hot but not smoking. Drop asparagus into skillet; keep stirring so that it will not burn. Cook for 3 minutes. Lower heat and add the canned sliced mushrooms with their liquid. Simmer until done, not more than 10 minutes.

Chapter 9

SALADS

FRUIT—PROTEIN—VEGETABLE

SALADS add zip to slimming fare and afford appetite-allaying bulk. It is difficult to feel satisfied without having a sense of fullness, for this is part of the normal satisfaction of hunger. Salads fill the bill.

Salads may be served as a first course or with the main course of the meal. Fruit and gelatin salads may replace dessert.

The secret of success with green salads is to serve them very crisp, really cold, and to add the chilled dressing just prior to serving the salad.

If salad is to be the mainstay of the meal it must include a protein, such as chicken, fish, seafood, or cottage cheese. Fruit salad served with cheese or cottage cheese makes an appetizing luncheon, particularly in warm weather.

It takes the right dressing to complement the salad. Gourmet-type dressings need not be excessively high in calories.

The salad dressings included in the recipe section are a boon to dieters. Use Fruit Salad Dressing with fruit salads, Dieter's French Dressing on vegetable salads, and Cooked Salad Dressing in seafood, chicken, and potato salads. With a meal that is near the top limit on calories for reducing, use Zippy Salad Dressing, for this dressing has a negligible calorie count.

There are seasoned mixes on the market which are convenient to use. The calorie count of the dressing, made according to the recipe on package, is 85 per tablespoon.

Fruit Salads

MOLDED FRUIT SALAD

(Individual serving: 1 mold; 80 to 85 calories)

		Calories
Gelatin, unflavored	1 envelope	28
Cold water	½ cup	–
Boiling water	1 cup	–
Sugar	¼ cup	192
Salt	⅛ to ½ tsp.	–
Lemon juice	¼ cup	15
Fruit, diced, drained	1½ cups	200–250
Salad greens	3 cups	30
	6 *servings*	465–515

Soften gelatin in the cold water. Add hot water, sugar, and salt; stir until thoroughly dissolved. (Fruit juice may be used as part of the liquid; calorie count is additional unless it has been included in the count for the fruit. If fruit juice has been used as part of the liquid, decrease sugar accordingly.) Add lemon juice; cool; then chill gelatin until mixture begins to set. Add the prepared fruit, which has been well drained. Turn into 6 individual molds; chill. Unmold on crisp salad greens. The calorie count for this salad can be decreased by substituting a noncaloric sweetener for the sugar. If salad dressing is used, the calorie count is additional.

FRUIT PLATTER WITH CHEESE

(*Individual serving: ½ salad; 190 calories*)

		Calories
Peach, fresh	1 medium	35
Banana	½ medium	45
Cherries, sweet, fresh, pitted	¼ cup	25
Honeydew melon balls	1 cup (about 12)	50
Watercress	1 cup	10
Cheese, process American	2 slices, 3¼″ square ×⅛″ (2 oz.)	210
	2 servings	375

Peel and quarter the peach. Cut banana into chunks. Pit cherries and make balls of the honeydew melon. Arrange in an attractive pattern on a platter. Tuck in the watercress sprigs. Cut the cheese slices into triangles and arrange at edge of platter. Cottage cheese (1 cup) may be used in place of the processed cheese.

PARTY SALAD PLATE

(*Individual serving: 210 calories*)

		Calories
Peach slices, fresh	½ cup	30
Plum, halved, pitted	1, 2″ diameter	25
Cantaloupe balls	½ cup (6 or 7)	30
Red raspberries	⅛ cup	10
Romaine		10
Swiss cheese	1-oz. slice	105
		210

Prepare fruits; chill separately. At serving time arrange attractively on romaine. Cut the Swiss cheese into 4 small squares and overlap at side of plate. This salad is a fine choice for a party luncheon on a hot summer day. Serve with toasted Ry-Krisp, iced or hot tea, and chilled baked custard.

CHERRY FRUIT SALAD

(*Individual serving: 1 mold; 30 calories*)

		Calories
Cherry D-Zerta® Gelatin	1 envelope	36
	(*4-serving size*)	
Salt	⅛ tsp.	–
Cloves, ground	⅛ tsp.	–
Cinnamon	⅛ tsp.	–
Boiling water	2 cups	–
Cherries, pitted, quartered, unsweetened	¼ cup	25
Banana, sliced*	⅔ medium	60
	4 servings	121

Combine gelatin, salt, cloves, and cinnamon. Add boiling water; stir to dissolve. Chill until thickened. Fold in fruit. Pour into 4 individual molds. Chill until firm. Unmold on serving plates. Makes about 2⅓ cups or 4 servings.

® D-Zerta is a registered trademark of General Foods Corporation for Low Calorie Flavored Gelatin and Low Calorie Pudding & Pie Filling.
* Or use ½ cup diced drained dietetic apricot halves (30 calories). Individual serving: 1 mold; 30 calories.

UNDER-THE-SEA SALAD

(Individual serving: 1 mold; 35 calories)

		Calories
Lime D-Zerta Gelatin	1 envelope (4-serving size)	36
Boiling water	2 cups	–
Vinegar	½ tsp.	–
Cottage cheese	⅓ cup	80
Pears, canned, dietetic pack, drained, diced	8¼-oz. can (⅔ cup)	48
Salt	¼ tsp.	–
Ginger	⅛ tsp.	–
	5 servings	164

Dissolve gelatin in boiling water. Add vinegar. Pour ¼ cup of the mixture into *each* of 5 individual molds. Chill until set, but not firm. Combine cottage cheese, pears, salt, and ginger; set aside. Chill remaining gelatin mixture until slightly thickened. Then fold in cottage-cheese mixture. Spread over firm gelatin in molds. Chill until firm. Serve on crisp salad greens. Makes 2⅔ cups.

MELON AND PEAR SALAD

(Individual serving: 105 calories)

		Calories
Melon balls	¾ cup	40
Pears, canned, drained	1 medium half	35
Grapes, green seedless	10, halved	20
Endive, curly		5
Lemon juice	2 tsp.	3
		103

Fresh or frozen melon balls may be used. Use frozen melon balls just before they are completely defrosted. Cube the canned pear half. Combine melon balls, pear, and grapes. Serve on bed of curly endive. Use lemon juice as dressing. If frozen melon balls are packed in heavy sirup, rinse and drain them.

SPICED APPLE GRAPE SALAD

(*Individual serving: 1 mold; 30 calories*)

		Calories
Strawberry or Raspberry D-Zerta Gelatin	1 envelope (*4-serving size*)	36
Salt	⅛ tsp.	–
Cinnamon	⅛ tsp.	–
Nutmeg	⅛ tsp.	–
Boiling water	2 cups	–
Apples, peeled, diced*	⅔ cup	50
Grapes, seeded, cut*	3 tbsp.	30
	4 servings	116

Combine gelatin, salt, cinnamon, and nutmeg. Add boiling water; stir to dissolve. Chill until thickened. Then fold in fruits. Pour into 4 individual molds. Chill until firm. Unmold on crisp salad greens. Makes 2⅓ cups.

* Or use ⅔ cup canned, drained dietetic pears, diced (48 calories). Individual serving: 1 mold; 35 calories.

GRAPEFRUIT AND GREEN PEPPER SALAD

(Individual serving: 50 calories)

		Calories
Grapefruit sections	½ cup	40
Lettuce, shredded		5
Green pepper strips	2 strips, ½" long	4
		49

Use fresh or unsweetened canned grapefruit sections. Arrange on shredded lettuce. Garnish with the green pepper strips.

Protein Salads

(POULTRY)

TURKEY SALAD—DELUXE

(Individual serving: ½ cup; 120 calories)

		Calories
Turkey, canned, boned	5-oz. can	285
Radishes, sliced	⅓ cup	6
Celery, diced	½ cup	8
Onion juice (optional)	Few drops	–
Cooked Salad Dressing	2 tbsp.	30
Salt	To taste	–
Paprika	Dash	–
Salad greens	1½ cups	15
Carrot-curl garnish	½ carrot	10
	3 servings	354

Flake canned turkey. Combine with the prepared vegetables. Moisten with the Cooked Salad Dressing; season to taste. Chill for a short time. Mound on salad greens; garnish with the carrot curls. This recipe provides 3 servings of ½ cup each; if a large luncheon salad is desired, it provides 2 servings of ¾ cup each. Individual serving: 175 calories.

CHICKEN SALAD

(*Individual serving: 180 calories*)

		Calories
Chicken, cooked	½ cup	150
Celery, diced	¼ cup	4
Cucumber, diced	¼	7
Seasonings (salt, pepper, paprika, celery seed, onion juice)	To taste	–
Cooked Salad Dressing	1 tbsp.	15
Lettuce		5
		181

Dice chicken. (Turkey may be used.) Add diced vegetables. Season to taste; add Cooked Salad Dressing. Serve on crisp lettuce.

CHICKEN SALAD—PARTY STYLE

(*Individual serving: 200 calories*)

		Calories
Chicken, cooked, diced	½ cup	150
Celery, diced	¼ cup	4
Grapes, green seedless, halved	10	20
Olives, green, chopped	1 large	5
Cooked Salad Dressing	1 tbsp.	15
Lettuce nest		5
Watercress		–
		199

Combine diced chicken with celery, grapes, and olives. Moisten with the Cooked Salad Dressing. Chill. Serve in crisp lettuce nest. Garnish with watercress sprigs.

(*FISH AND SHELLFISH*)

SHRIMP SALAD

(*Individual serving: 150 calories*)

		Calories
Shrimp, cooked or canned, cleaned	7 (2½ oz.)	80
Celery, sliced	2 medium stalks	10
Green pepper strips	½ pepper	7
Tomato, diced	1 small	25
Thousand Island Dressing	1½ tbsp.	22
Lettuce cup		5
		149

Combine the prepared shrimp with the vegetables; moisten with the Thousand Island Dressing; chill a short time. Serve in crisp lettuce cup.

TUNA FISH SALAD WITH GRAPES

(*Individual serving: ½ cup, large; 120 calories*)

		Calories
Tuna fish, dietetic pack	½ cup	91
Egg, hard-cooked	1 medium	80
Celery, diced	¼ cup	4
Grapes, green seedless	10	20
Salt	To taste	–
Cooked Salad Dressing	2 tbsp.	30
Lettuce cups		10
	2 servings	235

Drain and flake tuna fish. Cook and chop egg. Dice celery and halve the grapes. Combine ingredients; add salt to taste and blend in the Cooked Salad Dressing. Serve mounded in the lettuce cups. Canned, water-packed Bing cherries are a delicious substitute for the green seedless grapes (¼ cup, 30 calories). Total recipe: 245 calories. Individual serving: 125 calories. Be sure to add the drained Bing cherries just before serving; if allowed to stand any length of time after mixing the salad, the tuna fish will turn purple!

CRABMEAT SALAD

(*Individual serving: ½ cup; 100 calories*)

		Calories
Crabmeat, canned	7½-oz. can	215
Celery, finely minced	½ cup	8
Green pepper, chopped	2 tbsp.	4
Radishes, sliced	4 small	5
Lemon juice	1 tbsp.	4
Salt	To taste	–
Pepper	Dash	–
Cooked Salad Dressing	¼ cup	60
Chicory		5
	3 *servings*	301

Drain and flake crabmeat. Combine with the prepared vegetables; add lemon juice. Season to taste with salt and pepper. Chill. Just before serving, mix in the Cooked Salad Dressing. Serve on chicory.

Variations: Diced cucumber may be used in place of the green pepper. Add 1 hard-cooked egg, diced, for an additional 80 calories. The salad mixture may be used to stuff tomatoes which have been quartered not quite through.

TUNA FISH SALAD

(Individual serving: ½ cup; 140 calories)

		Calories
Tuna fish, canned, drained	1 cup	400
Egg, hard-cooked, chopped	1	80
Celery, diced	½ cup	8
Cucumber, diced	¼ cup	5
Sweet cucumber pickle, chopped	1, 2″ long	15
Salt	To taste	–
Pepper	Dash	–
Lemon juice	1½ tsp.	2
Cooked Salad Dressing	2 tbsp.	30
Lettuce	¼ head	15
	4 servings	555

Drain tuna fish. Flake fish into medium bowl. Add chopped hard-cooked egg, diced celery and cucumber, chopped pickle, and seasonings. Sprinkle with the lemon juice; mix in the Cooked Salad Dressing. Chill. At serving time, mound on crisp lettuce. If salad is served to 3, each serving of ¾ cup will contain 185 calories.

Note: If all oil is washed off tuna fish, the calorie count will be lower. If dietetic-pack tuna, which is canned without oil, is used, the calorie count of a ½-cup serving of salad will be approximately 85.

Salmon Salad: Canned salmon (1 cup, 390 calories) may be used in place of tuna fish in this salad. Total count of recipe: 545 calories. Individual serving of ½ cup: 135 calories.

SEAFOOD SALAD

(Individual serving: 75 calories)

		Calories
Lemon D-Zerta Gelatin	1 envelope (4-serving size)	36
Salt	1 tsp.	–
Boiling water	2 cups	–
Vinegar	2 tsp.	1
Tuna, flaked, dietetic pack*	1 cup	182
Celery, chopped	2 tbsp.	2
Green pepper, chopped	2 tbsp.	4
Onion, chopped	2 tsp.	2
	3 servings	227

Dissolve gelatin and salt in boiling water. Stir in vinegar; chill until thickened. Fold in remaining ingredients. Pour into small loaf pan or 3-cup mold. Chill until firm. Unmold. Garnish with crisp greens. Makes 2½ cups or 3 entrée servings.

* Crabmeat may be substituted for the tuna: 1 cup, 170 calories. Individual serving of salad with crabmeat: 70 calories.
If diced shrimp is used: 1 cup, 145 calories.
Individual serving of salad with shrimp: 65 calories.

(EGGS)

EGG SALAD IN TOMATO CUPS

(Individual serving: 1 tomato; 135 calories)

		Calories
Eggs, hard-cooked	3 medium	240
Celery, chopped fine	¼ cup	5
Pimiento, chopped	½ medium	5
Onion (scallion), minced	1	4
Cooked Salad Dressing	2 tbsp.	30
Salt	To taste	–
Pepper	Dash	–
Tomatoes	3 medium, 2×2½″	105
Lettuce, Boston	½ head	15
	3 servings	404

Chop hard-cooked eggs; combine with celery, pimiento, and onion. Moisten with the Cooked Salad Dressing; season to taste. Chill. At serving time place each tomato on bed of lettuce, stem end down; cut in quarters, not quite through. Fill centers with egg salad.

Vegetable Salads

BEET AND ONION SALAD

(Individual serving: 60 calories)

		Calories
Beets, cooked or canned, drained, sliced	⅓ cup	20
Chicory		5
Onion (scallion), sliced	1	4
French dressing	½ tbsp.	30
		59

Arrange sliced beets on bed of chicory; top with the sliced onion, including part of the top. Drizzle the French dressing over all.

COLESLAW

(Individual serving: ½ cup; 25 calories)

		Calories
Cabbage, shredded	½ cup	12
Onion, minced (optional)	½ tsp.	–
Cooked Salad Dressing	1 tbsp.	15
Parsley		–
		27

Shred cabbage; add minced onion to the salad dressing, if desired. Toss cabbage with the salad dressing; garnish with parsley; or, the parsley may be chopped and added to cabbage.

Variations: Use half green cabbage and half red cabbage for slaw. Add 2 tablespoons chopped green pepper or chopped cucumber to cabbage.

SAVORY SLAW

(Individual serving: ½ cup; 45 calories)

		Calories
Cabbage, shredded	2 cups	48
Carrots, shredded	1 cup	45
Sugar	1 tbsp.	48
Vinegar	3 tbsp.	6
Salt	To taste	–
Pepper	To taste	–
Celery seed	½ tsp.	–
Cooked Salad Dressing	⅓ cup	80
Lettuce, loose-leaf	1 head	30
	6 *servings*	257

Combine shredded cabbage and carrots. Mix sugar and vinegar; add to slaw mixture with salt, pepper, and celery seed. Moisten with the Cooked Salad Dressing. Serve ½ cup mounds on lettuce.

CELERY STUFFED WITH COTTAGE CHEESE

(*Individual serving: 2 stalks; 50 calories*)

		Calories
Celery	4 medium stalks	20
Parsley, chopped	1 tbsp.	1
Cottage cheese	⅓ cup	80
Paprika	Sprinkle	–
	2 servings	101

Have celery stalks crisp and dry. If small inner stalks are used, do not remove leaves. Mix chopped parsley with cottage cheese; fill the celery-stalk grooves with the cheese; chill well. At serving time sprinkle cheese with paprika. Serve whole, or cut stalks into 2-inch to 3-inch pieces.

Variations: Substitute one of the following for the chopped parsley; revise calorie count according to ingredients used.

Chives, chopped	1 tbsp.	2
Green pepper, minced	1 tbsp.	2
Stuffed olive, chopped	1 large	5
Sweet pickle, chopped	1 tbsp.	15
Radishes, chopped	2 small	3

GARDEN SALAD

(*Individual serving: 1 mold; 15 calories*)

		Calories
Lime D-Zerta Gelatin	1 envelope	36
	(*4-serving size*)	
Salt	1 tsp.	–
Boiling water	2 cups	–
Vinegar	1 tbsp.	2
Cucumber, diced	⅔ cup	14
Celery, diced	½ cup	10
Green onions, cut fine	¼ cup	10
	5 servings	72

Dissolve gelatin and salt in boiling water. Add vinegar; chill until thickened. Fold in cucumber, celery, and onions. Pour into 5 individual molds. Chill until firm. Unmold. Makes 2⅔ cups.

TOMATO ASPIC SALAD

(Individual serving: 1 mold; 30 calories)

		Calories
Gelatin, unflavored	1 envelope	28
Cold water	¼ cup	–
Hot tomato juice	1½ cups	70
Onion, grated	1 tbsp.	6
Lemon juice	1 tbsp.	4
Salt	¼ tsp.	–
Worcestershire sauce (optional)	¼ tsp.	1
Pepper	Dash	–
Salad greens		20
	4 servings	129

Soften gelatin in the cold water; dissolve in the hot tomato juice. Add the seasonings and blend. Pour into 4 individual molds. Chill until firm. Unmold on the salad greens. No salad dressing is required.

Variation: Add 1¼ cups vegetables (½ cup finely diced celery, ½ cup shredded cabbage, ¼ cup chopped green pepper or cucumber).

CHEF'S SALAD

(*Individual serving: 205 calories*)

		Calories
Salad greens	As desired	10
Celery heart, diced	1 heart	10
French dressing	1 tbsp.	60
Tomato, quartered	1 small	25
Chicken, cut in strips	1 oz.	50
Cheese, process American, cut in strips	½ oz.	50
		205

Break chilled salad greens into salad bowl. Add diced celery. Pour dressing over greens and celery and toss *lightly*. Arrange quartered tomato, chicken, and cheese strips over top of greens. Serve immediately.

STUFFED TOMATO SALAD

(*Individual serving: 60 calories*)

		Calories
Stuffing:		
Celery, diced	¼ cup	4
Cabbage, shredded	¼ cup	6
Radishes, sliced	2 small	3
Cooked Salad Dressing	1 tbsp.	15
Tomato, quartered	1 small	25
Lettuce		5
Parsley		–
		58

Mix the vegetables for stuffing with the Cooked Salad Dressing. Peel tomato and quarter, cutting not quite through. Arrange on lettuce leaves; push the quarters apart and fill with the stuffing. Garnish with parsley sprigs.

SUNSET SALAD

(*Individual serving: 1 mold; 25 calories*)

		Calories
Orange D-Zerta Gelatin	1 envelope	36
	(*4-serving size*)	
Salt	⅛ tsp.	–
Boiling water	2 cups	–
Vinegar	1 tbsp.	2
Carrots, raw, coarsely grated	⅔ cup	30
Pineapple, canned dietetic pack, drained, diced	¼ cup	30
	4 servings	98

Dissolve gelatin and salt in boiling water. Add vinegar. Chill until thickened. Then fold in carrots and pineapple. Pour into 4 individual molds. Chill until firm. Unmold on crisp salad greens. Makes about 2⅓ cups.

DIETER'S POTATO SALAD

(*Individual serving: ⅔ cup; 100 calories*)

		Calories
Potatoes, cooked, diced	3 cups	300
Eggs, hard-cooked, diced	2 medium	160
Cucumber, diced	½	15
Celery, diced	½ cup	8
Onion, chopped	½ small	5
Salt	1 to 1½ tsp.	–
Pepper or paprika	Dash	–
Cooked Salad Dressing	⅓ cup	80
Lettuce, Boston	1 head	30
	6 *servings*	598

Mix and chill ingredients, except lettuce. At serving time arrange portions in lettuce cups; or serve on a lettuce-bordered platter or in a salad bowl lined with lettuce.

Salad Dressings

COOKED SALAD DRESSING

(Individual serving: 1 tablespoon; 15 calories)

		Calories
Flour	1 tbsp.	25
Sugar	2 tbsp.	96
Salt	1¼ tsp.	–
Red pepper	Speck	–
Mustard, prepared	1 tsp.	5
Salad oil (corn)	1 tbsp.	125
Water	1 cup	–
Eggs	2 medium	160
Vinegar	4 tbsp.	8
	Approx. 1¾ cups	419

Blend together flour, sugar, salt, red pepper, prepared mustard, salad oil, and water in top of double boiler. Cook over hot water, stirring constantly, until slightly thickened. Beat eggs slightly in small bowl; add vinegar gradually. Slowly add half of the hot sauce to egg-and-vinegar mixture, stirring constantly. Return to double boiler. Stir and cook over hot (not boiling) water until mixture coats a spoon. Overcooking after eggs have been added will cause dressing to curdle. Remove from heat at once and pour into jar. When cool, cover and refrigerate. To make a thicker dressing to use as a spread, increase flour to 2 tablespoons. Combine first 7 ingredients and cook over direct heat, stirring constantly, until thickened. From this point on, proceed as above. Add 25 calories to total recipe count.

Russian Dressing: To ¼ cup of Cooked Salad Dressing add 1 tablespoon catsup. One tablespoon dressing: 16 calories.

Gourmet Dressing: To ¼ cup Russian Dressing add ½ teaspoon horseradish (or to taste) and a dash of Worcestershire sauce. One tablespoon dressing: 16 calories.

Thousand Island Dressing: To ½ cup of Cooked Salad Dressing add 2 tablespoons chili sauce, 2 tablespoons chopped green pepper, and ½ hard-cooked egg, chopped. One and a half tablespoons dressing: 22 calories.

FLUFFY COOKED SALAD DRESSING

(Individual serving: 2 tablespoons; 30 calories)

		Calories
Eggs, separated	2 medium	160
Sugar	2 tsp.	32
Butter, melted	1 tbsp.	100
Skim milk	⅔ cup	60
Vinegar	¼ cup	8
Salt	2 tsp.	–
Cayenne	Few grains	–
Dry mustard	1 tsp.	–
Cornstarch	2 tsp.	20
Skim milk	⅓ cup	30
	1½ to 2 cups	410

Separate eggs. In the top of a double boiler beat together the egg yolks, sugar, melted butter, the ⅔ cup of skim milk, vinegar, salt, cayenne, and dry mustard.

Dissolve cornstarch in the ⅓ cup of skim milk. Add to ingredients in double boiler. Cook and stir the dressing over boiling water until it is thick. Fold it into the 2 egg whites which have been stiffly beaten. Recipe makes from 1½ to 2 cups dressing; 15 calories per tablespoon.

FRUIT SALAD DRESSING

(Individual serving: 1 tablespoon; 21 calories)

		Calories
Pineapple juice	¼ cup	35
Orange juice	¼ cup	30
Lemon juice	3 tbsp.	12
Eggs	2 medium	160
Salt	⅛ tsp.	–
Sugar	2 tbsp.	96
	1 cup	333

Combine fruit juices in top of a double boiler; heat over boiling water. In a small bowl beat the eggs slightly with a fork; beat in the salt and sugar. Slowly stir a little of the hot fruit juices into egg mixture, while stirring constantly. Return all to double boiler and cook 2 minutes longer over hot (not boiling) water, stirring constantly. Cool and chill.

ZIPPY SALAD DRESSING
(Fat-free)

(Individual serving: 2 tablespoons; 6 calories)

		Calories
Onion, chopped	1 tbsp. (or less)	4
Green pepper	½ tsp.	–
Carrots, raw, chopped	¼ cup	12
Parsley	1 tsp.	–
Sucaryl solution	⅓ tsp.	–
Tomato juice	1 cup	45
Vinegar	¼ cup	8
Salt	To taste	–
Pepper	To taste	–
	1½ cups	69

Chop all vegetables finely. Combine all ingredients in a jar with a tightly fitted top. Shake till blended. Refrigerate, covered. Shake well before using.

Note: For a low-salt diet use tomato juice canned without salt, and a salt substitute for seasoning.

DIETER'S FRENCH DRESSING

(Individual serving: 1 tablespoon; 60 calories)

		Calories
Salad oil (corn)	½ cup	972
Tarragon or wine vinegar	½ cup	17
Dry mustard	½ tsp.	–
Celery salt	As desired	–
Salt	To taste	–
Pepper	To taste	–
Paprika (optional)	To taste	–
	1 cup	989

Combine ingredients in glass jar or bottle. Shake until blended. Store in refrigerator. Shake well before using. If sweetening is desired, add a few drops of Sucaryl solution.

Dieter's Roquefort French Dressing: To ¼ cup Dieter's French Dressing add ½ ounce crumbled Roquefort cheese. Individual serving: 1½ tablespoons, 90 calories.

Miscellaneous Recipes

(SAUCES)

CREOLE SAUCE

		Calories
Butter or margarine	1 tbsp.	100
Onion, chopped	1 small	10
Green pepper, chopped	½ medium	7
Tomatoes, canned	1-lb. can	95
Sugar	1 tsp.	16
Bay leaf	Tip	–
Whole clove	1	–
Salt	½ to 1 tsp.	–
Pepper	Dash	–
	2 cups	228

Melt butter in a medium skillet; add chopped onion and green pepper. Cook about 3 minutes, stirring to prevent burning. Add tomatoes, sugar, bay leaf, and whole clove. Season to taste with salt and pepper. Simmer, covered, about 20 minutes. Remove bay leaf and clove. The sauce may be strained, if desired.

Variations: A small can of drained, sliced mushrooms may be added to the sauce for the latter part of the cooking period. Bouillon made from a cube and hot water may replace part of the canned tomatoes. Use fresh tomatoes, if available, instead of canned. Chopped celery may be cooked in the butter with the onion and green pepper. Add a dash of chili powder for seasoning if desired.

LOW-CALORIE WHITE SAUCE

		Calories
Butter or margarine	2 tsp.	68
Flour	1 tbsp.	25
Salt	¼ to ½ tsp.	–
Pepper	Dash	–
Paprika (optional)	Dash	–
Skim milk	1 cup	90
	1 cup	183

Melt butter in a saucepan over *low heat*, or use double boiler. Add flour and seasonings; stir until blended and smooth. Add skim milk slowly; stir constantly until mixture thickens and is smooth. If sauce must stand, place it over hot water and cover tightly.

BARBECUE SAUCE

(Individual serving: 2 tablespoons; 20 calories)

		Calories
Butter or margarine	1½ tsp.	50
Onion, chopped	1 small	10
Green pepper, chopped	½ medium	7
Tomato sauce, canned	½ cup	36
Vinegar	2 tsp.	1
Worcestershire sauce	¼ tsp.	1
Horseradish (optional)	To taste	–
	⅝ cup	105

Melt butter in a small skillet; cook chopped onion and green pepper until soft. Add remaining ingredients; simmer about 10 minutes. Season with salt and pepper if necessary. Stir occasionally to prevent sticking.

DIETER'S CHEESE SAUCE

(Individual serving: 2 tablespoons; 30 calories)

		Calories
Butter or margarine	½ tbsp.	50
Flour	1½ tbsp.	38
Skim milk	1 cup	90
Salt	¼ tsp.	–
Paprika (optional)	Speck	–
Cheese, diet process American, grated	½ slice (½ oz.)	40
	1 cup (16 tablespoons)	218

Melt butter in saucepan over *low heat*, or use double boiler. Blend in flour. Add skim milk gradually, stirring constantly until smooth. Add seasonings. Cook until sauce begins to thicken. Add grated cheese, stir and cook until cheese is melted. Yield: 1 cup. One tablespoon sauce: 14 calories. Dieter's Cheese Sauce is an excellent base for casserole dishes.

LOW-CALORIE MACARONI AND CHEESE

(*Individual serving:* ⅔ *cup;* 190 *calories*)

		Calories
Macaroni, elbow, dry	1 cup	455
Butter or margarine	1 tbsp.	100
Flour	1 tbsp.	25
Salt	¼ tsp. plus	–
Pepper	Dash	
Skim milk	1½ cups	135
Cheese, process American, cubed	1 cup (¼ lb.)	420
Paprika	Sprinkle	–
	6 *servings*	1135

Cook macaroni according to package directions; drain. In a saucepan, melt butter; stir in flour, salt to taste, and pepper; blend. Add skim milk gradually and cook until mixture is smooth and heated through. Stir in the cubed cheese. Mix sauce with the drained macaroni. Place in a lightly greased casserole; sprinkle with paprika. Bake in a 350° oven until thoroughly heated through and lightly browned on top, about 45 minutes.

CHEESE SOUFFLÉ

(Individual serving: ¾ cup; 225 calories)

		Calories
Butter or margarine	2 tbsp.	200
Flour	2 tbsp.	50
Skim milk	1 cup (8 oz.)	90
Paprika (or few grains cayenne)	⅛ tsp. paprika	–
Salt	½ tsp.	–
Cheese, process American, grated	¾ cup (3 oz.)	315
Eggs, separated	3 medium	240
	4 servings	895

Melt butter; stir in flour; blend well. Add skim milk and seasonings. Cook, stirring constantly, until the mixture thickens. Add grated cheese; stir until it is melted. Remove from heat; add beaten egg yolks, beating vigorously. Combine mixture with beaten whites. Pour into a lightly greased baking dish. Set in pan of hot water; bake slowly in 300° to 350° oven until set, from 45 minutes to 1 hour. Serve immediately.

Variation: Add a small amount of minced vegetable, such as pimiento or onion, to the soufflé just before combining with the egg whites.

LOW-CALORIE COCOA

(Individual serving: 1 cup; 95 calories)

		Calories
Sugar	1 tsp.	16
Salt	Few grains	–
Cocoa	2 tsp.	14
Water	¼ cup	–
Skim milk	¾ cup	66
		96

Combine sugar, salt, cocoa, and water in the top of a small double cooker. Cook over direct heat until thick, from 2 to 4 minutes. Add the skim milk, which may be scalded if desired; place over hot water until thoroughly heated. Beat with rotary beater to prevent formation of film on surface of cocoa.

The calorie count of this recipe can be reduced by substituting ⅛ teaspoon Sucaryl solution for the 1 teaspoon sugar. Combine Sucaryl solution with the water, and cook the cocoa, water, salt, and Sucaryl solution *not more than 2 minutes* over direct heat, stirring constantly. Add skim milk and heat over hot water. One cup: 80 calories.

Chapter 10

CHOICE DESSERTS FOR
WEIGHT WATCHERS

DESSERTS would be an unalloyed delight if it were not for calories and corpulence. The happy solution is to have in your repertoire of recipes choice desserts that give calories the light touch.

A column reader hit upon a gladsome philosophy that adds zest to slimming fare. The dessert suggestion of "ambrosia" she took to mean anything one's heart desires within the dessert calorie quota. This is an ingenious way to avert dietitis, that worrisome malady that keeps you feeling uneasy about the fattening effects of delicious food *even while you are eating it*. When the grand finale to the meal is delectable and low in calories too, dessert can taste absolutely ambrosial.

Balanced meals are the key to both reducing and weight control. It is definitely a mistake to slight the main course in order to save more calories for a dessert. Not only would you shortchange yourself nutritionally, but you would be hungry again before long. It has been known for years that a meal high in carbohydrates, particularly in sugar, leaves the stomach much more rapidly than does a mixed diet. Protein and the more complex starches furnished in potato, bread, and vegetables must be broken down further; therefore, the fuel is released more slowly, and hunger assuaged for hours longer. Meals dominated by dessert defeat dieting.

Sweets, eaten by themselves, are even more undesirable. In small quantities they do not have satiety value, and when eaten in excess they turn into fat.

A sweet taste has a way of running to excess. It is important to understand the body's physical reaction. Sweets furnish quickly absorbable sugar which forces the blood sugar level high and in turn stimulates the secretion of insulin. Sugar burns quickly, so the blood sugar level falls rapidly and you feel hungry again. Any food will quell hunger, but if your preference is for something sweet, and that is what you eat, the cycle is repeated. You can never conquer your sweet tooth by indulging in assorted sweets.

Once you are alert to this fact, you recognize the necessity to stop the powerful stimulus to insulin secretion that is perpetuating the craving. Forgo candy and sugary rich desserts and you stop triggering this reaction.

The most jubilant reducers are those who find, to their complete amazement, that they really have conquered the compulsion to overeat on sweets.

In this push-button age it is intelligent to give desserts the light touch. As calories have become easily accessible and irresistible, the chances to work them off in physical activity have lowered markedly. The result is creeping overweight, in all age groups.

Today's loving wife and mother is the one who helps her husband to be happy on less fattening fare, and encourages the children to form good food habits.

The desserts in this section are designed for happy slimming.

Frozen Desserts

RASPBERRY-ORANGE SHERBET

(Individual serving: ½ cup; 80 calories)

		Calories
Raspberries, red, frozen, semithawed	10-oz. carton	275
Orange juice	1 cup	120
Lemon juice	2 tbsp.	8
Sugar	¼ cup	192
Egg whites, beaten	3	45
	8 servings	640

Thaw the frozen raspberries until they can be blended with the orange and lemon juices. Add the sugar; fold in the well-beaten egg whites. Turn into a chilled refrigerator tray; freeze until mushy. Remove to a chilled bowl and beat well with rotary or electric beater. Freeze until firm. If the sherbet is frozen in a deep freeze, it will be necessary to let it stand at room temperature for a brief period before serving. The calorie count of this recipe can be decreased by substituting 1½ teaspoons Sucaryl solution for the ¼ cup sugar. In this case, add ¼ cup water to the fruit juices and freeze the mixture to the *firm* stage before beating; refreeze until firm. Individual serving: ½ cup; 55 calories.

ORANGE FREEZE

(Individual serving: ½ cup, plain; 40 calories)

		Calories
Vanilla D-Zerta Pudding	1 envelope	64
	(4-serving size)	
Orange juice	1 cup	120
Orange D-Zerta Gelatin	1¾ tsp.	18
	(½ envelope)	
Salt	⅛ tsp.	–
Boiling water	½ cup	–
Egg whites	2	30
	6 servings	232

Place pudding mix in saucepan. Add ¼ cup of the orange juice. Stir until *thoroughly* blended. Add remaining orange juice. Cook and stir over medium heat until mixture comes to a boil. Remove from heat.

Dissolve gelatin and salt in boiling water. Combine with pudding mixture and chill until mixture thickens. Pour into a freezing container or shallow pan. Freeze until mixture forms ice crystals around edge and is thick in center. Place mixture in a chilled bowl; beat with rotary beater until smooth. Beat egg whites until they form stiff shiny peaks; fold into pudding mixture. Return to freezing container and freeze until firm, stirring occasionally. Let stand at room temperature about 15 minutes before serving. Serve plain or with fresh fruit. Makes about 3 cups.

This is a nice party dessert—you may wish to double the quantity for such an occasion, or to freeze in two containers, one for future use.

Fruit Desserts

AMBROSIA

(Individual serving: 145 calories)

		Calories
Orange, sliced	1 medium	75
Orange juice	¼ cup	30
Coconut, shredded	1 tbsp.	38
		143

Arrange orange slices in dessert dish; pour juice over orange. Sprinkle with the coconut; chill. Fresh coconut can be used.

FRUIT NECTAR FRUIT CUP

(Individual serving: ¾ cup; 90 calories)

		Calories
Malaga grapes	1 cup	95
Bananas, sliced	2	170
Pineapple chunks, canned	24 medium	125
Apricot nectar, canned	1 cup	140
	6 servings	530

Set out 6 serving cups. Seed and halve the grapes; put a portion in each cup. Slice one-third banana into each cup. Add 4 pineapple chunks to each cup. Pour the apricot nectar over the fruit. Refrigerate fruit cups until serving time.

ORANGE PUDDING

(Individual serving: ½ cup; 80 calories)

		Calories
Vanilla D-Zerta Pudding	1 envelope	64
	(4-serving size)	
Nonfat milk (skim milk)	1½ cups	135
Orange juice	½ cup	60
Oranges, sectioned and diced	2	150
	5 servings	409

Place pudding mix in saucepan. Add ¼ cup of the milk. Stir until *thoroughly* blended. Add remaining milk and the orange juice. Cook and stir over medium heat until mixture comes to a boil. Cool 5 minutes; fold in diced oranges. Pour into serving dishes or a bowl. Chill. (Pudding thickens as it cools.) Makes about 2½ cups.

If whole milk is used in preparation of pudding, the ½ cup serving will count 105 calories.

Variation: Banana-Orange Pudding

Prepare Orange Pudding as directed, substituting 1 banana, sliced, for the diced oranges. Individual serving: 70 calories.

If whole milk is used in preparation of pudding, the ½ cup serving will count 90 calories.

BROILED GRAPEFRUIT

(Individual serving: 1 half; 85 calories)

		Calories
Grapefruit (pink)	1 medium	120
Brown sugar	1 tbsp.	50
	2 *servings*	170

Select grapefruit heavy with juice. Preheat broiler. Halve grapefruit and remove seeds. Loosen pulp from membrane by running a very sharp knife completely around each section, without cutting into the white membrane. Place grapefruit halves on shallow pan on broiler rack. Top with the brown sugar. Broil slowly (from 3 inches to 4 inches under heat) until sugar is melted, the grapefruit heated through, and the edges lightly browned, 20 minutes or more. Serve hot.

Variations: Honey (½ tablespoon: 32 calories) may be used in place of the brown sugar. Sherry may replace the brown sugar. Remove core of grapefruit; pour 1 tablespoon sherry (20 calories) into the center. Broil.

MELON-BALL FRUIT CUP

(Individual serving: 50 calories)

		Calories
Honeydew melon balls	¼ cup (3 or 4)	12
Cantaloupe balls	½ cup (6 or 7)	30
Blueberries	⅛ cup	10
Mint sprig		–
		52

Combine chilled melon balls in serving cup; sprinkle with the blueberries. Garnish with mint sprig.

MELON RING WITH RASPBERRIES

(Individual serving: 1 ring, with berries; 85 calories)

		Calories
Cantaloupe, cut into 3 rings, 1" thick	1 5" diameter	120
Raspberries, red, fresh	¾ cup	50
	3 *servings*	170

Wash and dry melon; refrigerate in plastic or paper bag. Prepare raspberries; chill. At serving time cut melon into rings; remove seeds and membrane; peel rings. Place each ring on serving plate; fill center with ¼ cup fresh red raspberries.

PEACHES WITH MERINGUE

(Individual serving: 1 peach half; 60 calories)

		Calories
Peaches, canned	6 medium halves	210
Brown sugar	1 tbsp.	50
Lemon rind, grated	To taste	–
Egg white, beaten	1	15
Sugar	2 tbsp.	96
	6 *servings*	371

Drain canned peaches. Place 6 halves on an oven-proof platter, hollow side up. Sprinkle halves with the brown sugar and lemon rind. Make a meringue of the egg white and 2 tablespoons sugar. Spoon meringue on peach halves in peaks. Broil or bake until peaches are heated through and meringue is delicately browned. A dash of nutmeg or mace may be used in place of the lemon rind.

BAKED PEAR DELICIOUS

(*Individual serving: 1 pear; 150 calories*)

		Calories
Pears, fresh	4 medium	400
Sugar	¼ cup	192
Water	½ cup	–
Lemon juice and strip of rind	1 tbsp.	4
	4 servings	596

Wash pears; remove blossom ends, but leave stems on. Place in deep casserole with sugar, water, lemon juice and strip of rind. Cover and bake at 400° for 20 minutes. Reduce heat to 350° and bake until done (about 1 hour). Remove from oven and take up in individual serving dishes. If a noncaloric sweetener is used in place of the sugar, the value of 1 serving will be 100 calories.

FRESH PINEAPPLE DELUXE

(*Individual serving: ¼ pineapple; 95 calories*)

		Calories
Fresh pineapple	1, 4¼×4″	185
Sugar, granulated	1 tbsp.	48
Banana, sliced	1 medium	85
Red grapes	4 small clusters (5 grapes each)	50
Blueberries, fresh	¼ cup	20
	4 servings	388

Chill a ripe fresh pineapple. Cut into quarters, lengthwise, leaving the leafy top intact. Remove hard core from each section. Run a sharp knife between shell and fruit, loosening but without removing fruit. Cut the loosened fruit into 3 or 4 lengthwise strips; then cut strips crosswise into bite-size pieces. Sprinkle lightly with the sugar. Leave each serving of pineapple in its shell and center on dessert plate. Arrange the banana slices, grape clusters, and blueberries as an attractive garnish for the pineapple. Sweet cherries, strawberries, or raspberries, or other fruit in season may be substituted for the grapes and blueberries.

Variation: Omit granulated sugar. Mix 2 teaspoons of dark brown sugar (34 calories) with 2 teaspoons of pure rum extract. Drizzle mixture over pineapple. Let set a few minutes before placing on serving plates. Omit the added fruits. Individual serving: 55 calories.

Gelatin Desserts

RASPBERRY BAVARIAN

(Individual serving: 1 sherbet glass; 100 calories)

		Calories
Raspberry gelatin	3-oz. package	330
Boiling water	1 cup	–
Cold water	¾ cup	–
Lemon juice	3 tbsp.	12
Raspberries, red, frozen, thawed, drained	¾ cup	205
Nonfat dry milk, instant	3 tbsp.	47
Ice-cold water	3 tbsp.	–
	6 *servings*	594

Thaw a package of frozen raspberries. Dissolve gelatin in the boiling water; add cold water and lemon juice. Refrigerate until mixture begins to thicken. Drain the raspberries, reserving the juice. Beat the nonfat dry milk with ice-cold water until consistency of whipped cream. Beat gelatin until frothy. Fold whipped milk into gelatin; add the drained raspberries carefully. Spoon into 6 sherbet glasses. Chill. If desired, 1 tablespoon of the raspberry juice (15 calories) may be spooned over top of each serving.

APRICOT WHIP

(Individual serving: 1 mold; 35 calories)

		Calories
Apricot halves, canned, dietetic pack	2 8-oz. cans	160
Orange D-Zerta Gelatin	1 envelope (4-serving size)	36
Boiling water	1 cup	–
Lemon juice	1 tbsp.	4
Rum extract	¼ tsp.	–
	6 servings	200

Drain apricots, measuring liquid; add water to make 1 cup. Chop apricots and set aside. Dissolve gelatin in boiling water. Add measured liquid, lemon juice, and rum extract. Chill until slightly thickened. Place in bowl of ice and water; whip with rotary beater until fluffy and thick. Fold in chopped apricots. Pour into 6 individual molds. Chill until firm. Makes 4¾ cups.

SPANISH CREAM

(Individual serving: 1 mold; 85 calories)

		Calories
Gelatin, unflavored	1 envelope	28
Cold skim milk	2 cups	180
Sugar	3 tbsp.	144
Salt	⅛ tsp.	–
Eggs, separated	2 medium	160
Vanilla	1 tsp.	8
	6 servings	520

Soften gelatin in the cold skim milk in top of double boiler. Place over boiling water. Add sugar and salt; stir until gelatin and sugar are dissolved. Separate eggs. Beat yolks slightly; slowly beat in a small amount of the hot mixture; return to double boiler; cook over simmering water until eggs have thickened mixture; stir constantly. Remove from heat; add vanilla; chill until mixture begins to set. Beat egg whites until stiff; fold the gelatin mixture into the beaten whites. Spoon into 6 individual molds; chill until firm. Unmold on serving dishes. Or the dessert may be spooned into sherbet glasses either before or after chilling.

Variations: Almond extract may be used with or instead of the vanilla. A bit of grated orange rind may be used with the vanilla. A small amount of nutmeg may be used as part of the flavoring.

APPLE GINGER-UPPER

(Individual serving: ½ cup mold; 25 calories)

		Calories
Lemon or Strawberry D-Zerta Gelatin*	1 envelope (*4-serving size*)	36
Boiling water	1 cup	–
Low-calorie ginger ale	1 cup	1
Red apples, unpeeled, finely diced	1½ cups	125
	6 servings	162

Dissolve gelatin in boiling water. Stir in ginger ale. Chill until thickened. Fold in apples. Pour into small loaf pan or 6 individual molds. Chill until firm. Unmold. Makes 3 cups.

* Or use any red flavor.

DIETER'S CHEESECAKE

(Individual serving: 1¾" wedge; 115 calories)

		Calories
Gelatin, unflavored	2 envelopes	56
Sugar	¾ cup	578
Salt	¼ tsp.	–
Eggs, separated	2 medium	160
Skim milk	1 cup	90
Lemon rind, grated	1 tsp.	–
Cottage cheese, small curd	3 cups	715
Lemon juice	1 tbsp.	4
Vanilla	1 tsp.	8
Ice-cold water	½ cup	–
Nonfat dry milk, instant	½ cup	125
Graham cracker crumbs	⅓ cup	143
Cinnamon	⅛ tsp.	–
Nutmeg	⅛ tsp.	–
	16 servings	1879

Mix gelatin, sugar, and salt together thoroughly in the top of a double boiler. Beat together the egg yolks and 1 cup skim milk. Add to gelatin mixture and cook over boiling water, stirring constantly until gelatin is thoroughly dissolved, about 8 minutes. Remove from heat; add the grated lemon rind; cool. Beat cottage cheese with electric beater until well blended. (Or sieve.) Stir into gelatin mixture; add lemon juice and vanilla. Chill, stirring occasionally until mixture mounds slightly when dropped from a spoon. Fold in the egg whites, stiffly beaten.

Beat the ice-cold water and the nonfat dry milk together with a rotary beater until stiff and mixture stands in peaks.

Fold into gelatin mixture. Turn into a 9-inch pan and sprinkle top with a mixture of the graham cracker crumbs, cinnamon, and nutmeg. Chill until firm.

PINEAPPLE-LIME PARFAIT

(*Individual serving: 1 parfait glass; 95 calories*)

		Calories
Lime gelatin	3-oz. package	330
Boiling water	1 cup	–
Pineapple, canned, crushed	1 cup	195
Lemon juice	1 tbsp.	4
Ice-cold water	3 tbsp.	–
Nonfat dry milk, instant	3 tbsp.	47
	6 servings	576

Dissolve the gelatin in the boiling water. Drain crushed pineapple, reserving juice. Refrigerate crushed pineapple. Add the lemon juice to the pineapple juice; add enough cold water to make 1 cup of liquid. Add to gelatin. Chill until gelatin begins to thicken. Fold the drained pineapple into about two-thirds of the gelatin. Divide it into 6 parfait glasses. Beat the reserved gelatin until light. Beat the ice-cold water and the nonfat dry milk until thick; fold into the whipped gelatin. Pile on top of the parfait glasses. Chill. This is a party-pretty dessert. If larger servings are desired, use 5 parfait glasses; each serving will count 115 calories.

PINEAPPLE FLUFF

(Individual serving: 1 mold; 45 calories)

		Calories
Pineapple slices, canned, dietetic pack	14-oz. can	230
Lemon D-Zerta Gelatin	1 envelope (4-serving size)	36
Boiling water	1¼ cups	–
Noncaloric sweetener*	To equal 2 tsp. sugar	–
Water	6 tbsp.	–
Lemon juice	1 tbsp.	4
Nonfat dry milk	6 tbsp.	94
	8 *servings*	364

Finely cut pineapple slices, reserving liquid in can. Drain cut pineapple thoroughly, measuring liquid. Add reserved liquid and cold water, if necessary, to equal ¾ cup. Dissolve gelatin in boiling water. Stir in measured liquid and sweetener. Chill until slightly thickened. Combine water and lemon juice in small deep bowl. Sprinkle dry milk over top. Beat with rotary beater until consistency of whipped cream; fold in slightly thickened gelatin mixture. Then fold in pineapple. Pour into 8 individual molds or sherbet glasses. Chill until firm. Unmold, if necessary. Makes 4¼ cups.

* See Table of Sugar Equivalencies, page 243.

Puddings

CINNAMON CHOCOLATE MOUSSE

(Individual serving: ½ cup; 50 calories)

		Calories
Chocolate D-Zerta Pudding	1 envelope	55
	(*4-serving size*)	
Cinnamon	½ tsp.	–
Nonfat milk (skim milk)	2 cups	180
Egg whites	2	30
Sugar	2 tbsp.	96
	7 servings	361

Place pudding mix and cinnamon in saucepan. Add ¼ cup of the milk. Stir until *thoroughly* blended. Blend in remaining milk. Cook and stir over medium heat until mixture comes to a boil. Remove from heat. Beat egg whites until foamy throughout. Add sugar gradually and beat until mixture forms soft rounded peaks. Stir pudding gradually into egg whites, blending well. Spoon into serving dishes. Chill until set. Makes about 3½ cups.

If whole milk is used in preparation of pudding, the ½ cup serving will contain 70 calories.

LOW-CALORIE BAKED CUSTARD

(Individual serving: 1 custard cup; 100 calories)

		Calories
Skim milk, scalded	2 cups	180
Eggs	2 medium	160
Sugar	3 tbsp.	144
Salt	⅛ tsp.	–
Vanilla	½ to 1 tsp.	4 to 8
Nutmeg	Sprinkle	–
	5 servings	492

Preheat oven to 325°. Scald skim milk. Beat eggs, sugar, and salt until blended; add scalded milk and vanilla. Strain into 5 lightly buttered custard cups. (A fine way to grease any dish is to wipe it with the paper wrapper from ¼ pound butter.) Place cups in a pan of hot, not boiling, water to the depth of 1 inch. Sprinkle with nutmeg. Bake until custard is set, about 40 minutes. Serve warm or cold.

The calorie count of this recipe may be decreased by substituting Sucaryl for the sugar. Dissolve 1½ teaspoons Sucaryl solution or 12 crushed Sucaryl tablets in 2 tablespoons of the milk. Scald remaining milk in top of double boiler. Beat eggs until frothy. Stir in vanilla and a few drops of vegetable coloring, if desired. Add dissolved Sucaryl and the hot milk; mix well. Proceed as above, baking the custard in a 300° oven for about 1 hour. Serve cold. Total count of recipe: 348; individual serving: 70 calories.

Variations: Place a bit of light brown sugar in the custard cups before filling with the custard. One teaspoon brown sugar: 17 calories.

Coffee Custard: Dissolve 3 teaspoons instant coffee in 3 tablespoons of the scalded skim milk; return to the remaining scalded milk. You may use ¼ teaspoon almond extract for the flavoring. Serve cold.

Grape-Nuts Custard: Place 1 teaspoon Grape-Nuts cereal in bottom of each custard cup. Individual serving: 105 calories.

BLACK AND GOLD PARFAITS

(Individual serving: ½ cup; 60 calories)

		Calories
Butterscotch D-Zerta Pudding	1 envelope (4-serving size)	62
Nonfat milk (skim milk)	2 cups	180
Chocolate D-Zerta Pudding	1 envelope	55
Nonfat milk (skim milk)	2 cups	180
	8 servings	477

Place butterscotch pudding mix in saucepan. Add ¼ cup of the milk. Stir until *thoroughly* blended. Add 1¾ cups milk. Cook and stir over medium heat until mixture comes to a boil. Cool 5 minutes. Stir; chill until set.

Place chocolate pudding mix in saucepan. Add ¼ cup milk. Stir until *thoroughly* blended. Add 1¾ cups milk. Cook and stir over medium heat until mixture comes to a boil. Cool 5 minutes. Stir; chill until set.

Whip puddings separately until creamy. Spoon alternate layers of chocolate and butterscotch puddings into parfait or sherbet glasses. Makes about 4 cups.

If whole milk is used in preparation of pudding, the ½ cup serving will contain 95 calories.

MOCHA PUDDING

(Individual serving: ½ cup; 60 calories)

		Calories
Chocolate D-Zerta Pudding	1 envelope	55
	(4-serving size)	
Cold water	1 cup	–
Brewed coffee	1 cup	–
Whipped topping mix	1 envelope	360
Cold milk	½ cup	80
Vanilla	½ tsp.	4
	8 servings	499

Place pudding mix in saucepan. Add ¼ cup of the water. Stir until *thoroughly* blended. Blend in remaining cold water and the coffee. Cook and stir over medium heat until mixture comes to a boil. Cover surface with wax paper. Cool thoroughly. Prepare whipped topping mix with milk and vanilla as directed on package; blend into cooled pudding mixture. Chill. Makes about 4 cups.

*   *   *

BUTTERSCOTCH REFRIGERATOR COOKIES

(Individual serving: 1 cookie; 45 calories)

		Calories
Flour, all-purpose, sifted	1 cup	400
Baking powder, double-acting	½ tsp.	2
Salt	Dash	–
Butter	¼ cup	400
Brown sugar	2 tbsp.	100
Butterscotch D-Zerta Pudding	1 envelope (*4-serving size*)	62
Egg	1	80
Vanilla	¼ tsp.	2
	2 *dozen cookies*	1046

Sift flour with baking powder and salt. Cream butter and sugar; gradually add pudding mix, mixing thoroughly. Add egg and beat until mixture is light and fluffy. Add vanilla; then add flour mixture and mix well. Place dough on wax paper and shape into a roll about 2 inches in diameter. Wrap in wax paper and chill in freezer for 30 minutes or in refrigerator overnight—until firm enough to slice. Cut into ⅛-inch slices; place on baking sheet and bake at 375° for 8 to 10 minutes, or until cookies just begin to darken slightly around edges. Makes about 2 dozen cookies.

Chapter 11

DIETETIC FOODS—A BOON
TO DIETERS

THE surprise ingredient in any weight-control program should be pleasure. The food industry has brought out a pleasing variety of low-calorie foods. While such foods should never be thought of as reducing, for no food can reduce weight, they do enable you to indulge in taste-satisfying extras.

There are a number of low-calorie salad dressings, such as French-type dressing, Italian dressing, and blue-cheese dressing, which furnish 3 to 5 calories per teaspoon. A whipped diet dressing, a mayonnaise type, has 6 calories per teaspoon. These salad dressings are so low in calories as to be almost negligible on that score. Their use leaves room for other foods.

Important note: It must be emphasized that these special dressings do not provide the poly-unsaturated fatty acids furnished in liquid vegetable oils. If your doctor has prescribed a fat-controlled diet for the purpose of lowering cholesterol levels, be sure to include the amount of liquid vegetable oil stipulated in your diet. The dietary-type dressings can be used as extras.

The artificially sweetened jams, jellies, and marmalades are a welcome addition to breakfast. Some of them taste delightful and furnish only 1½ to 5 calories per teaspoon. These low-calorie preserves are possible because of the nonnutritive sweeteners used.

The wide variety of artificial sweeteners comes in liquid, tablet, and powder form. A table of sugar equivalencies is given on page 243.

Low-calorie gelatin and pudding desserts were among the original foods offered to weight watchers. The puddings come in butterscotch, chocolate, and vanilla flavors. Dessert gelatins include cherry, lemon, lime, orange, raspberry, and strawberry flavors. Low-calorie whipped toppings are a delightful addition to slimming fare, whether used as toppings or incorporated into low-calorie dessert recipes.

Diet-type soft drinks taste very much like the original product. These carbonated beverages contain 1 to 5 calories per bottle and are available in assorted flavors: cola, grape, ginger ale, lemon, root beer, orange—take your choice.

Dietetic-pack tuna fish is a calorie saver. A half cup of this water packed product furnishes only 91 calories.

It is good news for weight watchers when high-calorie foods such as nuts and cheese can be rendered less fattening through a special process.

Food technologists have succeeded in extracting 80 percent of the oil from peanuts, thus lowering their calorie content to that extent. The nuts are restored to their original shape, with little change in flavor. These new process peanuts are in test-market now.

Experiments with other types of nuts, notably pecans and English walnuts, have proved remarkably satisfactory. While these special nuts are not yet available, it is hoped they will be soon. The calories will be appreciably lower.

In the cheese line, there is a low-calorie processed American cheese on the market. This cheddar-type special-process cheese is 25 percent lower in calories than the regular product. A soft-type Neufchâtel cheese on the market contains 25 percent fewer calories than cream cheese.

Whipped butter and whipped margarine are available. These aerated products are lower in calories-per-volume measure than the regular products.

A so-called "imitation" margarine is in the offing. There is question as to the legality of using this label and the matter is now before the courts. In this special-process product the fat content is cut in half, which lowers the calories. This is not due to a whipping process, but to a filler used so that the resulting product has a texture similar to table spread.

The calorie content of dietetic foods is clearly marked on the labels. Some foods are labeled "low calorie" but with no calorie count stated. The term "lower in calories" is relative and has no real significance. In the near future, manufacturers of foods for which the claim of lower calorie content is made may be required to specify the number of calories.

Chapter 12

HOW TO LIVE HAPPILY
SLIM EVER AFTER

WEIGHT CONTROL is a way of eating, and a most enjoyable way it can be. Fortunately, the protective foods, which are essential to good nutrition, are not the fatteners.

Eating should be a delight, particularly when calories are curbed. The weight-control technique is to lessen the fattening ingredients in "made" dishes so there will be fewer calories per forkful. Plan well-balanced, appealing meals. With nutrition know-how and culinary ingenuity you can be a superb cook and keep the calories on the safe and svelte side.

At the finish of a reducing regime, you will not want anything like the quantities of food you formerly craved. To keep the upper hand on appetite, never deliberately overeat. Actually, it isn't pleasant to eat until you are surfeited, for thirty minutes later you get the full impact. Then you feel stuffed, dull, and uncomfortable. Re-educate your food habits and you can keep slim by habit. You no longer associate good eating with overeating. Scientific studies show that continued control of food intake can have a lasting effect on body-weight regulation.

DON'T OVEREAT—DON'T UNDEREXERCISE

Appreciate the role exercise plays in physical fitness and in holding the weight line. Without exercise, the battle of the bulge is less likely to stay won. Fat has an affinity for soft muscles. Even normal weights often err on the side of too little exercise, and they are not fit, for too much of their weight is in flabby fat.

If you have exercise activities that you thoroughly enjoy, you're in clover. Toned muscles impart an extra fillip of fine feeling. How about "game-scaping" the back yard so as to have a home playground for the whole family? Shuffleboard, badminton, quoits, croquet, and basket ball are all possibilities. Swimming is perfect, for it exercises all the little and big muscles without straining any. If you have access to a pool, swim regularly.

Not everyone can swim. It isn't even easy to get sufficient walking. But it is imperative that exercise in one form or another be woven into daily living. Pull up a rocker. The medical profession claims that televisionitis is frightfully fattening. During the commercials, viewers head for the refrigerator, almost on signal.

One doctor, an Englishman, prescribed an exercise break during commercials. He said, "Stir, stretch, straighten the spine, bring the postural muscles into play. Shake loose the limbs, change the focus of the eyes, unclench the jaw, and let life flow freely."

A one-minute stretch-session during the commercial could add up to "slimnastics." In a long-drawn-out stretch, muscles act against each other in a sort of tug-of-muscle.

Instead of sitting slumped in a lump, how about rocking-chair action? Rock for fifteen minutes during a program. Sit well back in the rocker, pull up and in with the brace of front muscles, and push vigorously with your feet. Rocking is a circulation rouser and surprisingly effective exercise.

HELP FOR POOR LOSERS

Dieters, if you fail to lose and feel discouraged, change the character of your meals. Hunger is the biggest hurdle. To control hunger, increase protein. Include one or two protein foods at each of the three meals, starting with breakfast. Food causes an increase in metabolism, protein more so than other foods. By eating a good breakfast, including protein, you get the benefits of increased metabolism all morning.

To control hunger, avoid concentrated sweets. Use carbohydrate in the form of vegetables, fruits, cereal, bread, or potato. Trim all fat from meats. Let the fat in the diet be in the form of oil in salad dressing, and for cooking, also in the small amount of margarine used.

Have a scientific pickup midmorning and midafternoon, preferably protein or fruit. A sweet will defeat your purpose, for this will be followed by a rebound to hunger.

Regular meal hours will help you to establish an appetite timeclock. Exercise will increase calorie expenditure. Get out and walk two miles a day. Soon you will look and feel like a new person.

Check with your doctor periodically. Follow his advice as to the number of pounds to reduce and the kind of exercise that is best suited to you. Improved health is the aim. Let your doctor help you.

REDUCING CLUBS BOOST MORALE

With dieting a national necessity, the reducing-club idea has spread with the momentum of a new hope. The camaraderie and friendly spirit of rivalry help sustain interest.

A national organization known as TOPS, which means Take Off Pounds Sensibly, was founded by Esther Manz. TOPS headquarters is located at 3180 South Twenty-seventh Street, Milwaukee, Wisconsin. There are branches in many cities throughout the nation. Write to TOPS headquarters for locations.

BANISH BOREDOM

Joy in living makes for success in slimming and staying slim. Let's face it, too much routine can lead to a rut, and ruts are deadly dulling. When you turn to food to assuage vague discontent, you cater to false appetite.

Action can banish boredom and give you a new outlook. Could you join a class? Adult education classes, scheduled for your convenience by your local school system, offer recreation and a chance to broaden your interests. The YWCA provides a wide variety of stimulating projects.

William James gave us the recipe for adding zest to everyday living: "Experiment, explore, change, grow! . . . It is excitement, ideas and efforts that restore energy and vitality to people." This challenging philosophy is the very heart of his teaching.

Stretch your mind to a new dimension. It's your life; why

not make it purposeful and joyous? Nobody else can sing your song the way you can sing it.

To stay enthusiastically on the right course, keep the picture of a slim, trim, vital you vividly in mind. With your verve renewed, you'll feel recharged with energy.

Make the calories count for positive, wholesome, salubrious health to be genuinely enjoyed. Intelligent eating, not rigid dieting, is the key to weight control.

So, eat to build healthy leanness, exercise to feel zestful, and you can achieve desirable weight and live happily slim ever after.

III

Calorie

Chart

NEW CALORIE VALUES

TABLES OF food composition evolve with the changing times. The calories values in the recipes and in the Calorie Chart have all been brought up to date in order to conform with the newly revised edition of Agriculture Handbook No. 8.

The most nearly representative values for year-round products in country-wide use are given. The major changes have been in data for fruits, vegetables, and meats. The new edition of the Handbook shows proportions of separable lean and separable fat as part of the description of each cut of meat.

Over the years changes occur in animal breeding and food processing that may effect changes in energy-yielding nutrients, thus changing calorie values.

The new publication reflects advances in analytical techniques and progress in the food industry. Many new foods have been added to the table, bringing the total to nearly 2500 items.

REFERENCES USED IN COMPILING
THE CALORIE CHART

Composition of Foods, Raw, Processed, Prepared, by Bernice K. Watt and Annabel L. Merrill. U.S. Department of Agriculture Handbook 8. Revised edition, 1963. U.S. Government Printing Office, Washington, D.C.

Nutritive Value of Foods, U.S. Department of Agriculture Home and Garden Bulletin No. 72. Revised edition, 1964. U.S. Government Printing Office, Washington, D.C.

Food and Your Weight, by Louise Page and Lillian J. Fincher. U.S. Department of Agriculture Home and Garden Bulletin No. 74. Revised edition, 1964. U.S. Government Printing Office, Washington, D.C.

Food, The Yearbook of Agriculture 1959. U.S. Department of Agriculture. U.S. Government Printing Office, Washington, D.C.

Canned Food Tables. National Canners Association, 1965. Washington, D.C.

The authors wish to thank the following food companies for furnishing food analyses of their products:
Arnold Bakers, Inc., Greenwich, Connecticut
Burry Biscuit Company, Elizabeth, New Jersey
Campbell Soup Company, Camden, New Jersey
Cream of Wheat Corporation, Minneapolis, Minnesota
General Foods Corporation, White Plains, New York
H. J. Heinz Company, Pittsburgh, Pennsylvania
Hershey Chocolate Corporation, Hershey, Pennsylvania
Kellogg Company, Battle Creek, Michigan
Charles B. Knox Gelatine Company, Inc., Johnstown, New York
Kraft Foods Company, Chicago, Illinois
Thomas J. Lipton, Inc., Englewood Cliffs, New Jersey
National Biscuit Company, New York, New York
Pepperidge Farm Inc., Norwalk, Connecticut
Ralston Purina Company, St. Louis, Missouri
Sunshine Biscuits, Inc., Long Island City, New York
S. B. Thomas, Inc., Long Island City, New York
United Biscuit Company of America, Melrose Park, Illinois
The Wheatena Corporation, Rahway, New Jersey

BEVERAGES

		Calories
Carbonated beverages		
Club sodas	6-oz. glass	–
Cola type	6-oz. glass	70
Cream sodas	6-oz. glass	75
Fruit-flavored sodas	6-oz. glass	80
Ginger ale	6-oz. glass	55
Root beer	6-oz. glass	75

		Calories
Chocolate beverages		
Commercial		
Chocolate milk drink		
Made with whole milk	1 cup (250 gm.)	210
Made with skim milk	1 cup (250 gm.)	190
Homemade		
Hot chocolate, made with whole milk	1 cup (250 gm.)	240
Hot cocoa, made with whole milk	1 cup (242 gm.)	235
Chocolate beverages prepared from commercial mixes		
Hot chocolate-flavored drink	1 oz. mix plus water	115
Instant cocoa	2 heaping tsp. mix (⅔ oz.) plus 1 cup whole milk	230
	2 heaping tsp. mix (⅔ oz.) plus 1 cup skim milk	160
Chocolate milk shake	1 milk shake	330
Cider, sweet	6-oz. glass	90
Coffee, black	1 cup	–
With 1 lump sugar, 1⅛×¾×⅜″		25
With 1 tsp. sugar		16
With 1 tbsp. light cream		30
With 1 tbsp. evaporated milk		20
With 1 tsp. cream substitute, dried		11

Eggnog
  6 oz. milk
  1 egg
  2 tsp. sugar
	1 serving	230

Fruit juices: See pages 209–10		

Lemonade
  1 oz. lemon juice
  2 tbsp. sugar
	1 large glass	105

		Calories
Metrecal Liquid Diet	8-oz. glass	225
Metrecal Powder	2 oz. (Add water)	225
Milk beverages		
Buttermilk	1 cup (246 gm.)	90
Whole milk, fresh (3.7% fat)	8-oz. glass (244 gm.)	160
Skim milk	8-oz. glass (246 gm.)	90
Milk, partially skimmed, with 2% nonfat milk solids added	8-oz. glass (244 gm.)	145
Milk, half whole, half skim	8-oz. glass (245 gm.)	125
Liquid milk (prepared from instant nonfat dry milk)	8-oz. glass	81–82
Malted milk beverages		
Natural flavor	1 large glass (270 gm.) (1 oz. powder plus 1 cup whole milk)	275
Chocolate	¾ oz. powder plus 1 cup whole milk	245
Chocolate malted milk shake	1 milk shake	445
Nutrament (commercial liquid food)	12½-oz. can	400
Ovaltine, natural flavor	¾ oz. powder (77 cal.) plus 1 cup whole milk	235
	¾ oz. powder (77 cal.) plus 1 cup skim milk	165
Postum, Instant, clear	1 cup (155 gm.)	14
Soda, ice cream—chocolate	1 soda	285
Tea, clear	1 cup	–

BREADS

		Calories
Biscuits, baking powder		
Baked from home recipe	1, 2½″ diameter (38 gm.)	140
Baked from commercial mix	1, 2½″ diameter (38 gm.)	125
Biscuit dough, commercial, chilled in cans	1 biscuit, unbaked (23 gm.)	65
Boston brown bread	1 slice, 3×¾″ (48 gm.)	100
Corn bread		
Baked from commercial mix	Piece, 2″ square ×1½″ (45 gm.)	105
Spoonbread	½ cup (100 gm.)	195
Cracked wheat bread	1 slice, ½″ thick (23 gm.)	60
French or Vienna bread	1 slice, 1″ thick (20 gm.)	60
Hollywood bread	1 slice, ⅜″ thick (18 gm.)	46
Oatmeal bread		
Arnold oatmeal bread	1 slice (30 gm.)	83
Pepperidge Farm oatmeal bread	1 slice (25.5 gm.)	70
Raisin bread	1 average slice (23 gm.)	60
Rye bread		
American, light	1 slice, ½″ thick (23 gm.)	55
Pumpernickel	1-oz. slice	70
White bread		
Average 4% nonfat dry milk	1 slice, ½″ thick (23 gm.)	60
	1 thin slice (17 gm.)	45

		Calories
Arnold white bread		
Brick Oven	1 slice (23 gm.)	66
Hearthstone	1 slice (30 gm.)	87
Pepperidge Farm white bread		
English Tea Loaf	1 slice (25.5 gm.)	73
White sandwich loaf	1 slice (23 gm.)	68
Whole-wheat bread		
2% nonfat dry milk	1 slice, ½" thick (23 gm.)	55
Arnold whole-wheat bread		
Brick Oven	1 slice (23 gm.)	64
Hearthstone	1 slice (30 gm.)	85
Pepperidge Farm whole-wheat bread	1 slice (23 gm.)	67
Muffins		
Blueberry muffins	1, 2½" diameter (48 gm.)	135
Bran muffins	1, 2½" diameter (42 gm.)	110
Corn muffins	1, 2½" diameter (44 gm.)	140
Pancakes and waffles		
Buckwheat pancakes (baked from mix)	1, 4" diameter (27 gm.)	55
Wheat pancakes (baked from mix)	1, 4" diameter (27 gm.)	60
Waffles, baked	1, 6" diameter (75 gm.)	210
Rolls and similar breads		
Cinnamon buns, with raisins	1 average (60 gm.)	165
Danish pastry	3½-oz. piece	420
English muffins (Thomas)	1, 3" diameter (61.8 gm.)	140
Hamburger rolls	1 (45 gm.)	135
Hard rolls	1 large (52 gm.)	160
Hot dog rolls	1 (40 gm.)	120

		Calories
Pan rolls, commercial	1 (38 gm.)	115
Sweet rolls, pan, commercial	1 (43 gm.)	135
Miscellaneous breads		
Bread crumbs, dry, grated	1 cup (88 gm.)	345
Bread dressing (stuffing, from mix)	½ cup (100 gm.)	358
Bread sticks, Italian	1 long	39
Croutons		
Toasted	7 (5 gm.)	15
Fried	7 (7 gm.)	30
Pizza, with cheese (cheese topping)	5½″ sector (⅛ of 14″-pie) (75 gm.)	185
Popovers	1 average (50 gm.)	110
Toast		
Cinnamon toast	1 slice (36 gm.)	120
French toast (use no-stick pan, no fat)	1 slice (50 gm.)	100
Melba toast, commercial, plain	1 slice	16
	1 round	7–9

CEREALS

		Calories
Cooked cereals		
Corn grits, degermed	¾ cup (180 gm.)	90
Cornmeal, white or yellow, degermed	¾ cup (180 gm.)	90
Cream of Wheat, quick-cooking	¾ cup (180 gm.)	100
Farina, quick-cooking	¾ cup (180 gm.)	75
Oatmeal or rolled oats	⅔ cup (160 gm.)	107
Ralston's cereal	¾ cup (180 gm.)	97
Wheatena	¾ cup (180 gm.)	110

		Calories
Ready-to-eat cereals		
Bran (All-Bran)	½ cup (1 oz.)	98
	1 tbsp. (3.5 gm.)	12
Bran flakes (40%)	⅔ cup (1 oz.)	89
Bran flakes, with raisins	½ cup (1 oz.)	89
Corn flakes	1 cup (1 oz.)	110
Grape-Nuts cereal	¼ cup (1 oz.)	100
Grape-Nuts Flakes	⅔ cup (1 oz.)	100
Oat flakes	⅔ cup (1 oz.)	110
Rice, Puffed	1 cup (½ oz.)	55
Special K	1 cup (18 gm.)	66
Wheat flakes	¾ cup (1 oz.)	100
Wheat germ	1 oz.	125
Wheat, Puffed	1 cup (12 gm.)	44
Wheat, Shredded	1 biscuit (approx. ¾ oz.)	85
Bite-size	1 oz.	108

CEREAL PRODUCTS

		Calories
Cereal flours		
Biscuit mix, with enriched flour	1 cup (120 gm.)	510
Cornmeal, white or yellow, degermed, enriched	1 cup (145 gm.)	525
Wheat flours		
All-purpose or family	1 cup (110 gm.)	400
	1 tbsp. (7 gm.)	25
Cake or pastry flour	1 cup (100 gm.)	365
Whole-wheat flour	1 cup (120 gm.)	400
Macaroni, cooked (14 to 20 minutes)	1 cup (140 gm.)	155
Noodles		
Egg noodles, cooked	1 cup (160 gm.)	200

		Calories
Chow mein noodles, canned	½ cup (1 oz.)	140
Popcorn, popped, plain	1 cup (14 gm.)	55
Rice, cooked	½ cup (84 gm.)	90
Spaghetti, cooked (14 to 20 minutes)	1 cup (140 gm.)	155
Tapioca, dry	1 cup (152 gm.)	535
	1 tbsp. (10 gm.)	35

CEREAL PRODUCTS: PREPARED DISHES

Macaroni and cheese, baked from home recipe	1 cup (220 gm.)	470
Macaroni and Cheese "TV" Dinner, frozen (Swanson brand)	1 complete dinner (361 gm.)	367
Spaghetti with meat balls in tomato sauce, home recipe	1 cup (250 gm.)	335

CONDIMENTS, PICKLES, AND OLIVES

		Calories
Catsup, tomato, bottled	1 tbsp. (17 gm.)	20
Chili powder	1 tbsp. (15 gm.)	50
Chili sauce	1 tbsp. (17 gm.)	20
Curry powder	1 tsp., level (2 gm.)	4
Horseradish, prepared	1 tsp. (5 gm.)	2
Meat sauce (restaurant)	1 tbsp.	20
Mustard, brown, prepared	1 tsp., level (5 gm.)	5
Olives, pickled		
Green	4 medium or 3 extra large or 2 giant (16 gm.)	15

		Calories
Ripe: Mission	3 small or 2 large (10 gm.)	15
Pickles, cucumber		
Dill	1 large, 4×1¾″ (135 gm.)	15
Fresh (as bread-and-butter pickles)	4 slices (1 oz.)	20
Sweet	1 pickle, 2″ long, ⅝″ diameter (10 gm.)	15
Relish, sweet, chopped	1 tbsp. (20 gm.)	25
Soy sauce	1 tbsp. (15 gm.)	10
Worcestershire sauce	1 tsp. (5 gm.)	4

CRACKERS

		Calories
Animal crackers	1 (2.3 gm.)	10
Bacon Flavored Thins	1 (2.1 gm.)	10
Butter Thins	1 (3.2 gm.)	15
Cheese Ritz	1 (3.4 gm.)	17.6
Cheese Tid-Bits	1 (.9 gm.)	4
Cheese Peanut Butter Sandwich	1 packet (31.3 gm.) (4 sandwiches)	153
Club Crackers	1 piece (3.2 gm.)	15
French Onion Thins	1 (2.3 gm.)	11
Graham crackers		
Plain	1 (7.0 gm.)	30
Chocolate-coated	1 (13.7 gm.)	70
Graham cracker crumbs	1¼ cups (4.6 oz.)	535
Holland Rusk	1 (13 gm.)	53.9
Oyster crackers	10 (10 gm.)	45
Pretzels—Three Ring	1 (3.1 gm.)	11.6
Pretzel sticks	5 small (5 gm.)	20

		Calories
Ritz Crackers	1 (3.3 gm.)	17.6
Rye crackers		
Ry-Krisp		
Regular	1 triple wafer (6.3 gm.)	21
Seasoned	1 triple cracker (6.7 gm.)	25
Rye wafers, whole grain	2, 1⅞×3½″ (13 gm.)	45
Saltines	1 (3.2 gm.)	14.2
Sea Toast	1 piece (14.2 gm.)	60
Sesame crackers	1, 2⅝″ diameter (5 gm.)	20.5
Sociables crackers	1 (2.1 gm.)	10
Social Tea Biscuits	1 (4.5 gm.)	20.6
Soda crackers	1 (7.2 gm.)	30.7
Triangle Thins	1 (1.7 gm.)	8.1
Triscuit wafers	1 (4.4 gm.)	21.6
Vegetable Thins	1 (1.8 gm.)	8.9
Wheat Thins	1 (1.8 gm.)	9.3
Zwieback	1 piece (6.8 gm.)	30

DAIRY PRODUCTS AND EGGS

		Calories
Butter or margarine	1 cup (2 sticks) (227 gm.)	1625 (butter)
		(margarine) 1635
	1 tbsp., level (14 gm.)	100
	1 pat or square, 1¼×1¼×¼″ (7 gm.)	50
	1 tsp., level (4.7 gm.)	35
	½ pat (3.5 gm.)	25
Cheese		
Blue or Roquefort type	1 oz.	105

		Calories
Cheddar or American		
Ungrated	1 oz.	115
	1"-square cube (17 gm.)	70
Grated	1 cup (112 gm.)	445
	1 tbsp. (7 gm.)	30
Process American		
Regular	1-oz. slice 3¼" square × ⅛" (28 gm.)	105
Low-calorie	1-oz. slice	80
Cottage cheese		
Creamed	1 cup (225 gm.)	240
	½ cup (112 gm.)	120
	2 tbsp. (1 oz.)	30
Uncreamed	1 cup (225 gm.)	195
	½ cup (112 gm.)	95
	2 tbsp. (1 oz.)	25
Cream cheese	3-oz. pkg. (85 gm.)	315
	2 tbsp. (1 oz.)	105
	1 tbsp. (15 gm.)	55
Parmesan	1 oz.	107
Dry, grated	1 tbsp. (5 gm.)	20
Roquefort cheese	1 oz.	105
Cheese foods, Cheddar	1 oz.	90
Velveeta (loaf)	1 oz.	90
Nippy (link)	1 oz.	93
Cheese spreads, average	1 oz.	80
Old English	1 oz.	97
Swiss cheese		
Natural (domestic)	1 oz.	105
Process	1-oz. slice, 3¼" square × ⅛"	100

CHEESE: PREPARED DISHES

		Calories
Pizza (cheese)	5½″ sector (⅛ of 14″ pie, 75 gm.)	185
Cheese soufflé	1 cup (145 gm.)	315
Welsh rarebit	½ cup (125 gm.)	225
(Toast or crackers extra)		
Cream		
Half-and-half (cream and milk)	1 cup (242 gm.)	325
	1 tbsp. (15 gm.)	20
Light cream, coffee or table	1 cup (240 gm.)	505
	1 tbsp. (15 gm.)	30
Heavy whipping cream, unwhipped	1 cup (238 gm.)	840
	1 tbsp. (15 gm.)	55
Whipped, sweetened (2 tbsp. sugar to 1 cup cream)	2 tbsp., level	60
Cream substitutes, dried	1 tsp. (2 gm.)	11
Milk		
Buttermilk, cultured (made from skim milk)	1 cup (246 gm.)	90
Milk, whole, fresh (3.7% fat)	1 cup (244 gm.)	160
	1 tbsp. (15 gm.)	10
Skim milk	1 cup (246 gm.)	90
	1 tbsp. (15 gm.)	5
Milk, partially skimmed with 2% nonfat milk solids added	1 cup (244 gm.)	145
Chocolate milk		
Made with whole milk	1 cup (250 gm.)	210
Made with skim milk	1 cup (250 gm.)	190
Condensed milk, canned, sweetened, undiluted	1 cup (306 gm.)	980
	1 tbsp. (20 gm.)	60
Evaporated milk, canned, unsweetened, undiluted	6-oz. can (approx. ⅔ cup)	235
	1 tbsp. (16 gm.)	20

		Calories
Evaporated skimmed milk, canned	2 tbsp. (1 fluid oz.)	24
Milk, dry		
Whole	1 cup (103 gm.)	515
	1 tbsp. (16 gm.)	32
Nonfat (skim), instant	⅓ cup (23 gm.)	81–82*
	1 tbsp. (4 gm.)	15
Yogurt		
Made from whole milk	1 cup (246 gm.)	150
Made from partially skimmed milk	1 cup (246 gm.)	120
Eggs		
Raw		
Whole, without shell	1 large (50 gm.)	80
White of egg	1 (33 gm.)	15
Yolk of egg	1 (17 gm.)	60
Cooked		
Soft-cooked, hard-cooked, or poached (shell removed)	1 (50 gm.)	80
Deviled egg		
Standard recipe	1	140
Low-calorie	1 with 1 tsp. mayonnaise	115
Fried	1 with 1 tsp. fat	115
Omelet: 1-egg	1	125
1 egg		
1 tbsp. milk		
1 tsp. fat		
Omelet: 2-egg	1	250
2 eggs		
2 tbsp. milk		
2 tsp. fat		
Scrambled eggs	1 cup (220 gm.)	380
(Standard recipe)	½ cup (110 gm.)	190

* Brands vary.

		Calories
Scrambled egg (low-calorie)	1 serving	135
1 egg		
2 tbsp. milk		
1 tsp. fat		

DESSERTS

		Calories
Cakes		
Angel-food cake, baked from commercial mix	2″ sector (1/16 of 10″ cake, 43 gm.)	110
Boston cream cake	2″ sector (1/12 of 8″ cake, 66 gm.)	200
Cheesecake		
Standard recipe	Piece, 2½×4×2″ (115 gm.)	275
Low-calorie	1¾″ wedge (1/16 of 9″ cake, 80 gm.)	110
Chocolate cake (devil's food), with chocolate icing	1¾″ sector (1/16 of 9″ layer cake, 100 gm.)	370
Cupcake (plain cake), with chocolate icing	1, 2¾″ diameter (50 gm.)	185
Fruitcake	Piece, 2×2×½″ (30 gm.)	115
Gingerbread	Piece, 2×2×2″ (55 gm.)	175
Plain cake, with chocolate icing (home recipe)	1¾″ sector (1/16 of 9″ layer cake, 80 gm.)	295
Pound cake	Slice, 2¾×3×⅝″ (30 gm.)	140
Sponge cake	2″ sector (1/16 of 10″ cake, 47 gm.)	140
Yellow cake, with chocolate icing (from commercial mix)	1¾″ sector (1/16 of 9″ layer cake, 80 gm.)	270

Calories

Cookies
Animal crackers	1 (2.6 gm.)	12
Arrowroot biscuits	1 (4.8 gm.)	22
Brownies, home recipe	1-oz. piece	140
Chocolate chip cookies, commercial	1 (10.5 gm.)	50
Chocolate-covered grahams	1 (13.7 gm.)	70
Doughnuts, plain	1 average (32 gm.)	125
Fig bars	1 small (16 gm.)	55
Ginger snaps	1 (7 gm.)	30
Ladyfingers	1 double (10 gm.)	36
Lemon snaps	1 (3.8 gm.)	16
Meringue shells	1 large, 4″ diameter (30 gm.)	105
Molasses cookies (home recipe)	1, 3″ diameter × ½″ (26 gm.)	110
Nabisco Sugar Wafers	1 (3.5 gm.)	18
Oatmeal cookies (home recipe)	1 large, 3″ diameter (25 gm.)	115
Shortbread cookies, commercial	Piece, 1¾″ square (8 gm.)	40
Social Tea Biscuits	1 (4.5 gm.)	20
Sugar cookies (home recipe)	1, 3″ diameter × ½″ (25 gm.)	110
Vanilla wafers, commercial	1 (4 gm.)	18

Frozen desserts
Ice cream and frozen custard (12% fat)	¼ pint (½ cup) (71 gm.)	145
Ice milk	½ cup (94 gm.)	140
Ice, lime (water)	½ cup (96 gm.)	75
Sherbet, orange	½ cup (96 gm.)	130

Fruit desserts
Apple, baked (1 tbsp. sugar)	1 large, 3″ diameter	170
Apple brown Betty	½ cup (115 gm.)	175
Prune whip	⅔ cup (90 gm.)	140

		Calories
Strawberry shortcake	1 serving (2 tbsp. whipped cream)	400
Gelatin desserts		
D-Zerta Low Calorie Gelatin (any flavor)	½ cup (121 gm.)	9
Jell-O® Gelatin Dessert (any fruit flavor)		
Plain	½ cup (139 gm.)	81
With fruit added	½ cup (140 gm.)	94
Pastries		
Piecrust, plain, baked		
Lower crust	1 9″ shell (135 gm.)	675
Double crust	1 double crust, 9″ pie (270 gm.)	1350
Pies		
Apple	3½″ sector, ⅛ of 9″ pie (118 gm.)	300
Blueberry	3½″ sector, ⅛ of 9″ pie (118 gm.)	285
Cherry	3½″ sector, ⅛ of 9″ pie (118 gm.)	310
Chocolate meringue	3½″ sector, ⅛ of 9″ pie (120 gm.)	300
Coconut custard	3½″ sector, ⅛ of 9″ pie (114 gm.)	270
Custard	3½″ sector, ⅛ of 9″ pie (114 gm.)	250
Lemon meringue	3½″ sector, ⅛ of 9″ pie (105 gm.)	270
Mince	3½″ sector, ⅛ of 9″ pie (118 gm.)	320
Pumpkin	3½″ sector, ⅛ of 9″ pie (114 gm.)	240

® Jell-O is a registered trademark of the General Foods Corporation.

Calories

Miscellaneous pastries

Eclair—chocolate icing (custard filling)	1 average (85 gm.)	205
Cream puff (custard filling)	1 average (85 gm.)	200

Puddings

Custard, baked	½ cup (124 gm.)	140
Rennet dessert pudding	½ cup (135 gm.)	130
Rice pudding with raisins	½ cup (100 gm.)	145
Minute Tapioca Pudding	½ cup (164 gm.)	182

Puddings from commercial mixes

Cooked pudding & pie filling (chocolate)	1 serving (147 gm.) (4 from 1 package) (½ cup, generous)	182
Instant (chocolate)	1 serving (155 gm.) (4 from 1 package) (⅔ cup, scant)	194
	1 serving (124 gm.) (5 from 1 package) (½ cup, level)	155
Tapioca Puddings (any flavor)	½ cup (145 gm.)	166

D-Zerta Low Calorie Puddings

Butterscotch, Chocolate, or Vanilla

Made with whole milk	½ cup (127 gm.)	95
Made with nonfat milk	½ cup (127 gm.)	60

FATS AND OILS

Calories

Bacon fat	1 tbsp. (14 gm.)	125
Butter or margarine*	1 tbsp., level (14 gm.)	100

* See Dairy Products and Eggs, page 193.

		Calories
Fats, cooking		
Lard	1 cup (220 gm.)	1985
	1 tbsp. (14 gm.)	125
Vegetable fats	1 cup (200 gm.)	1770
	1 tbsp. (12.5 gm.)	110
Oils, salad or cooking	1 cup (220 gm.)	1945
	1 tbsp. (14 gm.)	125

FISH AND SHELLFISH*

For baked or broiled fish allow 6 ounces raw weight per serving. One pound, 2 ounces of raw fish, when cooked, yields three servings, approximately 5 ounces each.

In preparing fish, brush lightly with salad oil, melted butter, or margarine. Season with salt, pepper, and paprika.

Dieters should allow not more than one tablespoon of fat per pound of fish. This will add approximately 35 calories for one serving of fish.

		Calories
Anchovies, canned	4 thin fillets (16 gm.)	30
Anchovy paste	1 tsp. (7 gm.)	14
Bass, black sea, fillets		
Baked	4.93 oz. (139.77 gm.)	190
Broiled	4.89 oz. (138.63 gm.)	215
Bass, striped, fillets		
Baked	4.97 oz. (140.90 gm.)	205
Broiled	4.97 oz. (140.05 gm.)	205
Bluefish fillets		
Baked	4.77 oz. (135.23 gm.)	185
Broiled	4.87 oz. (138.06 gm.)	185

* Data on baked and broiled fish fillets and steaks was provided by the Bureau of Commercial Fisheries, Fish and Wild Life Service, U. S. Department of Interior. Material was received November, 1964.

		Calories
Caviar, canned, pressed	1 tbsp. (25 gm.)	80
Clams, raw, meat only	5 medium (100 gm.)	75
Cod, fresh, fillets		
Baked	4.09 oz. (115.95 gm.)	115
Broiled	4.01 oz. (113.68 gm.)	125
Crab		
"Fresh" (cooked, steamed)	3 oz. (85 gm.)	80
Canned	3 oz. (85 gm.)	85
Flounder fillets		
Baked	4.79 oz. (135.80 gm.)	155
Broiled	4.30 oz. (121.91 gm.)	165
Frog legs, fried	4 large (96 gm.)	280
Haddock fillets		
Baked	4.71 oz. (133.53 gm.)	140
Broiled	4.55 oz. (128.99 gm.)	140
Halibut steaks		
Baked	4.92 oz. (139.48 gm.)	145
Broiled	4.74 oz. (134.38 gm.)	130
Herring, smoked, kippered	1 small (100 gm.)	210
Lobster		
Cooked	1-lb. lobster (raw weight) (6 oz., edible portion, cooked weight)	160
Canned	3 oz. (85 gm.)	80
Mackerel fillets		
Baked	5.18 oz. (146.85 gm.)	180
Broiled	4.60 oz. (130.41 gm.)	190
Ocean perch fillets		
Baked	4.95 oz. (140.33 gm.)	190
Broiled	4.86 oz. (137.78 gm.)	195
Oysters		
Raw, meat only	½ cup (8 medium, 120 gm.)	80
Cooked, fried	3 oz. (85 gm.)	205
Oyster stew: See Soups, page 224		

Calories

Salmon steaks		
Baked	5.35 oz. (151.67 gm.)	190
Broiled	4.97 oz. (140.90 gm.)	195
Salmon, canned		
Pink	3 oz. (85 gm.)	120
Red	3 oz. (85 gm.)	145
Sardines, canned, drained	5 to 7 medium (3 oz.)	175
Scallops, raw	3½ oz. (100 gm.)	80
Shad fillets		
Baked	5.45 oz. (154.51 gm.)	270
Broiled	4.98 oz. (141.18 gm.)	330
Shrimp		
Raw	3½ oz. (100 gm.)	90
French-fried	3½ oz. (100 gm.)	225
Canned, meat only	3 oz. (85 gm.)	100
Sole, fillet of: See Flounder, page 202		
Swordfish steaks		
Baked	4.41 oz. (125.02 gm.)	215
Broiled	4.17 oz. (118.22 gm.)	210
Trout, brook, broiled	5 oz. (142 gm.)	145
Trout, lake, broiled	5 oz. (142 gm.)	240
Tuna, canned, drained		
Canned in oil	3 oz. (85 gm.)	170
Canned in water	3 oz. (85 gm.)	115
Whitefish fillets		
Baked	4.81 oz. (136.36 gm.)	205
Broiled	4.41 oz. (125.02 gm.)	185

PREPARED DISHES

Codfish cakes, frozen, fried, reheated	2-oz. cake	155
Crab cakes	1 serving (110 gm.)	230
Crab, deviled	1 serving (160 gm.)	295
Crab Imperial	⅔ cup (110 gm.)	155

		Calories
Crab salad	⅔ cup (approx. 4 oz.)	150
Fish 'n' French Fries "TV" Dinner, frozen (Swanson brand)	1 complete dinner (276 gm.)	429
Fish sticks, frozen, cooked	5 (4 oz.)	280
Filet of Haddock "TV" Dinner, frozen (Swanson brand)	1 complete dinner (347 gm.)	397
Salmon loaf	1 serving (135 gm.)	210
Scallop "TV" Dinner, frozen (Swanson brand)	1 complete dinner (227 gm.)	398
Shrimp, French fried, with batter coating	1 serving (75 gm.)	150
Fried Shrimp "TV" Dinner, frozen (Swanson brand)	1 complete dinner (213 gm.)	358
Tuna noodle casserole	1 serving (200 gm.)	280
Tuna Pie, frozen, commercial (Swanson brand)	1 (227 gm.)	453
Tuna salad	1 serving (225 gm.)	350

FRUITS

		Calories
Apples, raw*	1 medium, 2½″ diameter (150 gm.)	70
Cubed or sliced	½ cup (71 gm., E.P.)	40
Applesauce, canned		
Unsweetened	½ cup (120 gm.)	50
Sweetened	½ cup (127 gm.)	115
Apricots		
Fresh*	3 apricots (114 gm.)	55

* Gram weight is on fruit as purchased. Calorie values are on edible portions. E.P. is used to indicate that gram weight is based on edible portion only.

		Calories
Canned, sirup pack*	4 medium halves with 2 tbsp. sirup (122 gm.)	105
Dried, uncooked	10 small halves (38 gm.)	100
Cooked		
Unsweetened	⅓ cup (95 gm.)	80
Sweetened	⅓ cup (108 gm.)	130
Avocados, raw		
California varieties	½ peeled (108 gm.)	185
Florida varieties	½ peeled (123 gm.)	160
Bananas, raw	1 medium, 6×1½" (100 gm., E.P.)	85
Slices	¾ cup (116 gm.)	100
Blackberries		
Fresh	½ cup (72 gm.)	40
Canned, sirup pack	½ cup (126 gm.)	115
Blueberries		
Fresh	⅔ cup (93 gm.)	60
Canned, sirup pack	½ cup (124 gm.)	125
Cantaloupe*	½ melon, 5" diameter (385 gm.)	60
Balls	¾ cup (9 or 10) (150 gm.)	45
Cherries		
Dark sweet (Bing)		
Fresh, unpitted*	15 medium (95 gm.)	60
Canned, sirup pack*	⅓ cup (105 gm.)	80
Light sweet, canned, sirup pack*	½ cup (120 gm.)	90
Maraschino cherries	1 (3.7 gm.)	7
Red cherries		
Sweet, fresh, unpitted*	½ cup (65 gm.)	40
Sour, pitted, canned, sirup pack	½ cup (130 gm.)	115

* Fruits are canned in heavy sirup. Calorie values increase if fruits are packed in extra heavy sirup.

		Calories
Sour, pitted, canned, water pack	1 cup (247 gm.)	105
Cranberries, raw	1 cup (113 gm.)	50
Dates, pitted	2 (15 gm.)	40
Figs		
Fresh	3 small, 1½″ diameter (114 gm.)	90
Canned, sirup pack	3 with 2 tbsp. sirup (114 gm.)	95
Dried, uncooked	1 large, 2×1″ (21 gm.)	60
Fruit cocktail, canned, sirup pack	½ cup (128 gm.)	95
Fruit salad, canned, sirup pack, drained	1 serving, 1 piece each kind of fruit (3 oz.)	65
Grapefruit		
Fresh*		
White	½ medium (285 gm.)	55
Pink or red	½ medium (285 gm.)	60
Sections, white	½ cup (97 gm., E.P.)	40
Canned, sirup pack	½ cup sections with liquid (124 gm.)	85
Canned, water pack	½ cup sections with juice (120 gm.)	35
Grapes*		
American, slip skin (Concord)	1 cup (153 gm.)	65
European, adherent skin (Malaga, Tokay, Emperor)	1 cup (160 gm.)	95
Green seedless	1 medium bunch 40 grapes (135 gm.)	80
Honeydew melon	1 wedge 2×7″ (150 gm., E.P.)	50
Balls	¾ cup (9 to 10) (112 gm.)	35
Lemons*	1 medium (106 gm.)	20
Limes*	1 medium (68 gm.)	15

Calories

Melon balls		
Fresh fruit (cantaloupe, honeydew, watermelon)	¾ cup (140 gm.)	40
Frozen	4 oz.	36
Mixed fruits, frozen	4 oz.	124
Nectarines*	1 small (109 gm.)	65
Oranges*		
California navels	1 (180 gm.)	60
Florida oranges	1 (210 gm.)	75
Sections	½ cup (96 gm., E.P.)	45
Papayas	½ medium (182 gm.)	70
Peaches		
Fresh*	1 medium, 2″ diameter (114 gm.)	35
Sliced	¾ cup (126 gm., E.P.)	50
Canned, sirup pack	2 medium halves with 2 tbsp. sirup (117 gm.)	90
Frozen, sliced	4 oz.	99
Pears		
Fresh*	1, 3×2½″ diameter (182 gm.)	100
Canned, sirup pack	2 medium halves with 2 tbsp. sirup (117 gm.)	90
Persimmons*	1, 2½″ diameter (125 gm.)	75
Pineapple		
Fresh	1 slice (approx. ¾″×3½″ diameter) (84 gm.)	45
Diced	¾ cup (105 gm.)	55
Canned, sirup pack		
Chunks	10 medium, with 2 tbsp. juice (100 gm.)	75
Crushed	½ cup (130 gm.)	95
Slices	1 large or 2 small with 2 tbsp. juice (122 gm.)	90

Calories

Plums		
Fresh*	1, 2″ diameter (60 gm.)	25
Canned, sirup pack*	3 with 2 tbsp. juice (127 gm.)	100
Prunes, dried		
Uncooked*	4 medium (32 gm.)	70
Cooked, without added sugar*	4 medium, with 2 tbsp. juice (87 gm.)	95
Raisins, dried	1 tbsp., scant (10 gm.)	30
Raspberries, black, fresh	¾ cup (100 gm.)	75
Raspberries, red		
Fresh	¾ cup (92 gm.)	50
Frozen	5 oz.	138
Rhubarb, raw, diced	1 cup (122 gm.)	20
Strawberries		
Fresh, capped	¾ cup (112 gm.)	40
Frozen		
Halves	5 oz.	155
Whole	5 oz.	131
Tangerines*	1 medium, 2½″ diameter (114 gm.)	40
Watermelon		
Balls or cubes	¾ cup (9 or 10) (160 gm.)	40
Slices*	1, ¾×10″ (690 gm.)	80
Wedges*	1, 4×8″ (¹⁄₁₆ of 10×16″ melon) (925 gm.)	115

FRUIT JUICES

		Calories
Apple juice	½ cup (4 oz.)*	60
Apricot nectar	½ cup (4 oz.)	70
Cranberry juice cocktail, bottled	½ cup (4 oz.)	80
Grape juice		
Canned or bottled	½ cup (4 oz.)	85
Frozen concentrate, diluted	½ cup (4 oz.)	65
Grapefruit juice, white		
Fresh	¾ cup (6 oz.)	70
	½ cup (4 oz.)	50
Canned		
Unsweetened	¾ cup (6 oz.)	75
	½ cup (4 oz.)	50
Sweetened	¾ cup (6 oz.)	100
	½ cup (4 oz.)	65
Frozen concentrate, diluted		
Unsweetened	¾ cup (6 oz.)	75
	½ cup (4 oz.)	50
Sweetened	¾ cup (6 oz.)	90
	½ cup (4 oz.)	60
Lemon juice	¼ cup (4 oz.)	15
	1 tbsp. (15 gm.)	4
Lime juice	¼ cup (4 oz.)	15
	1 tbsp. (15 gm.)	4
Orange juice		
Fresh		
California Valencia	¾ cup (6 oz.)	90
	½ cup (4 oz.)	60

* The ounce values used for the fruit juices refer to fluid ounces, not weight ounces.

		Calories
Florida varieties		
Early and midseason	¾ cup (6 oz.)	75
	½ cup (4 oz.)	50
Late season, Valencia	¾ cup (6 oz.)	85
	½ cup (4 oz.)	55
Canned, unsweetened	¾ cup (6 oz.)	90
	½ cup (4 oz.)	60
Frozen concentrate,	¾ cup (6 oz.)	85
unsweetened, diluted	½ cup (4 oz.)	55
Orange and grapefruit juice		
Canned		
Unsweetened	¾ cup (6 oz.)	80
	½ cup (4 oz.)	55
Sweetened	¾ cup (6 oz.)	95
	½ cup (4 oz.)	65
Frozen concentrate,	¾ cup (6 oz.)	80
unsweetened, diluted	½ cup (4 oz.)	55
Peach nectar, canned	½ cup (4 oz.)	60
Pear nectar, canned	½ cup (4 oz.)	65
Pineapple juice, canned,	¾ cup (6 oz.)	105
unsweetened	½ cup (4 oz.)	70
Prune juice, canned or bottled	½ cup (4 oz.)	100
Tangerine juice		
Canned		
Unsweetened	½ cup (4 oz.)	55
Sweetened	½ cup (4 oz.)	60
Frozen concentrate,	½ cup (4 oz.)	55
unsweetened, diluted		
Tomato juice, canned	½ cup (4 oz.)	25

MEATS, COOKED

		Calories
Bacon, crisp, drained	1 medium slice (8 gm.)	50
	1 thin slice (5 gm.)	30

		Calories
Bacon, Canadian style	2 medium slices, 3″ diameter × ⅛″ (40 gm.)	110
	2 small slices, 3×2¼×¹⁄₁₆″ (24 gm.)	66
Beef		
Corned beef		
Cooked	3 oz.	315
Canned	2 slices, 3×2×⅜″ (1½ oz.)	90
Corned beef hash, canned	½ cup (115 gm.)	210
Dried beef, chipped	2 oz. (approx. ⅓ cup)	115
Ground beef, lean round, broiled (fat trimmed off before grinding)	4-oz. patty	215
	3½-oz. patty (4 from 1¼ lb. raw meat)	190
	3-oz. patty	160
Hamburger		
Lean	3½-oz. patty	220
	3-oz. patty	185
Regular	3½-oz. patty	285
Beef pot roast, chuck		
Lean	2 slices, 4×3×¼″ (3½ oz.)	195
Lean and fat	3½ oz.	290
Beef roast		
Rib roast		
Lean	2 slices, 4×3×¼″ (3½ oz.)	240
Lean and fat	3½ oz.	440
Rump roast		
Lean	2 slices, 4×3×¼″ (3½ oz.)	210
Lean and fat	3½ oz.	345
Sirloin tip roast		
Lean	4 oz.	235
	2 slices, 4×3×¼″ (3½ oz.)	205

		Calories
Lean and fat	3½ oz.	385
Beefsteak		
Club steak, broiled		
Lean	Piece, 4×2×1" (4 oz.)	275
Lean and fat	4 oz.	515
Flank steak, lean, braised	3½ oz.	195
Porterhouse, T-bone, Tenderloin, average, broiled		
Lean	Piece, 4×2×1" (4 oz.)	255
Lean and fat	4 oz.	525
Round steak, cubed, pan-broiled (added fat ½ tsp., 20 cal.)	Piece, 4×4×⅜" (3½ oz.)	210
Sirloin steak, broiled		
Lean	Piece, 4×2×1" (4 oz.)	235
Lean and fat	4 oz.	440
Beef stew meat (lean chuck), braised	4 oz.	245
Lamb		
Lamb chops, broiled*		
Loin chop		
Lean	1, ¾" thick, lean meat only (2 oz.)	105
Lean and fat	2 oz.	205
Rib chop		
Lean	1, ¾" thick, lean meat only (1½ oz.)	90
Lean and fat	1½ oz.	175

* The difference in calories on same weight of lamb chop is due to varying values on cuts of lamb.

Calories

Shoulder chop		
Lean	1, ¾" thick, lean meat only (3½ oz.)	205
Lean and fat	3½ oz.	340
Lamb roast (leg)		
Lean	2 slices, 4×3×¼" (3½ oz.)	185
Lean and fat	3½ oz.	280
Pork, fresh		
Pork chop, loin		
Lean	1, lean meat only (2 oz.)	155
Lean and fat	2 oz.	220
Pork roast, sirloin		
Lean	2 slices, 3½×2½×¼" (3½ oz.)	255
Lean and fat	3½ oz.	360
Pork spareribs, braised	3½ oz.	440
Pork, cured		
Ham, baked		
Lean	2 slices, 5×2½×⅛" (3 oz.)	160
Lean and fat	3 oz.	245
Sausages and miscellaneous meats		
Bologna	1-oz. slice	85
Chili con carne, canned		
With beans	⅔ cup (167 gm.)	220
Without beans	⅔ cup (170 gm.)	340
Deviled ham, canned	1½ tbsp. (1 oz.)	100
Frankfurter	1 frankfurter (51 gm.)	155
	1 small, 2" long (20 gm.)	60
Heart, beef, lean, braised	3 oz.	160
Kidneys, beef, braised	3½ oz.	250

		Calories
Liver, pan-broiled (lightly floured)		
Beef liver	2 slices, 3×2¼×⅜″ (3 oz.)	195
Calf liver	2 slices, 3×2¼×⅜″ (3 oz.)	220
Liver paste (*pâté de foie gras*), canned	1 tbsp., level (15 gm.)	70
Liverwurst	1-oz. slice	85
Luncheon meat		
Boiled ham	1-oz. slice	65
Chopped cured pork	1-oz. slice	85
Salami (cooked type)	1-oz. slice	90
Sausage, pork	1 link (15 gm.)	70
	1 patty, 2″ diameter (1½ oz.)	200
Sausage, Vienna, canned	1 oz.	70
Sweetbreads, braised		
Beef	3 oz.	270
Calf	3 oz.	145
Tongue, beef, braised	3 oz.	210
Veal		
Veal chop, loin, lean, broiled	1, ¾″ thick, lean meat only (3½ oz.)	235
Veal cutlet, lean, broiled	1, 4×2¼×½″ (3½ oz.)	215
Veal roast, rib	Slice, 4×4×⅜″ (3½ oz.)	270

PREPARED MEAT DISHES

Beef hash	¾ cup	260
Beef potpie	Individual pie,	560
Home-prepared, baked	4¼″ diameter (weight before baking about 8 oz.)	

		Calories
Commercial, frozen, unheated (Swanson brand)	Individual pie (8 oz.)	443
Beef and vegetable stew		
Cooked, home recipe (lean beef chuck)	1 cup (235 gm.)	210
Canned	1 cup (227 gm.)	180
Cheeseburger	1	365
Chop suey, with meat, cooked from home recipe	1 cup (250 gm.)	300
With ⅔ cup rice (125 calories)	1 serving	425
Croquette, ham	1 (3 oz.)	215
Dried beef, creamed	½ cup (120 gm.)	205
Gravy, with beef fat, flour	1 tbsp., rounded	35
Meat loaf	Slice, 4×3×½″ (3½ oz.)	200–350
Plate dinners, frozen, commercial		
"TV" Dinners (Swanson brand)		
Beans & Franks	1 complete dinner (305 gm.)	476
Beef	1 complete dinner (319 gm.)	423
Beef—3-Course Dinner	1 complete dinner (461 gm.)	602
Chopped Sirloin Beef	1 complete dinner (284 gm.)	447
Corned Beef Hash	1 complete dinner (284 gm.)	353
Ham	1 complete dinner (291 gm.)	366
Loin of Pork	1 complete dinner (284 gm.)	350

		Calories
Meat Loaf	1 complete dinner (284 gm.)	419
Mexican Style	1 complete dinner (461 gm.)	658
Salisbury Steak—3-Course Dinner	1 complete dinner (482 gm.)	520
Spaghetti & Meatballs	1 complete dinner (326 gm.)	323
Swiss Steak	1 complete dinner (326 gm.)	351

NUTS

		Calories
Almonds, dried, shelled	¼ cup (35 gm.)	210
	7 (10 gm.)	60
Brazil nuts, shelled	4 (10 gm.)	65
Cashew nuts, roasted	¼ cup (34 gm.)	190
	5 (10 gm.)	55
Chestnuts, fresh, shelled	1 oz. (28 gm.)	55
Coconut, flaked, packaged	¼ cup (1 oz.)	150
	1 tbsp. (7.1 gm.)	38
Filberts or hazelnuts	10 (10 gm.)	63
Macadamia nuts, shelled	¼ cup (30 gm.)	205
	6 (10 gm.)	70
Mixed nuts		
Shelled	¼ cup (32 gm.)	200
Dry, toasted	¼ cup (1 oz.)	173
Peanuts, roasted and salted	¼ cup (36 gm.)	210
	12 (10 gm.)	60
Peanut butter	1 tbsp. (16 gm.)	95
Pecans, shelled	¼ cup (27 gm.)	185
	5 halves (10 gm.)	70
Pistachio nuts, shelled	¼ cup (32 gm.)	190
	20 (10 gm.)	60

		Calories
Walnuts, English, shelled	¼ cup (25 gm.)	165
	6 halves (10 gm.)	65
Chopped	1 tbsp. (8 gm.)	50

POULTRY

		Calories
Chicken, broiled		
Meat only	3 oz. (85 gm.)	115
Meat and skin	¼ of 2-lb. broiler (3 oz. without bone)	190
Chicken, fried		
Meat only	½ breast (3 oz.)	165
Meat and skin	½ breast (3½ oz.)	205
	Thigh and drumstick (3 oz.)	225
Chicken, roasted		
Meat only	3 slices (3½ oz.)	185
Meat and skin	3½ oz.	250
Chicken (hen), stewed, diced, light and dark meat (no skin)	1 cup (5 oz.)	300
Chicken livers		
Raw	3 oz.	110
Baked or pan-fried (1 tsp. margarine)	3 small livers	145
Chicken, canned, boned	3 oz.	170
Turkey, roasted	2 slices, 4½×2½×¼″ (3½ oz.)	190

PREPARED POULTRY DISHES

Chicken à la King		
Home recipe	½ cup (125 gm.)	240
Frozen (Birds Eye)	¾ cup (85 gm.)	90

		Calories
Chicken chow mein (without noodles)	1 cup (245 gm.)	250
Chicken potpie, baked, home recipe	Individual pie, 4¼″ diameter (about 8 oz.)	535
Chicken or turkey salad	½ cup (3 oz.)	200
Plate dinners, frozen, commercial (Swanson brand)		
Fried Chicken "TV" Dinner	1 complete dinner (340 gm.)	600
Fried Chicken 3-Course Dinner	1 complete dinner (454 gm.)	652
Turkey "TV" Dinner	1 complete dinner (347 gm.)	401
Turkey 3-Course Dinner	1 complete dinner (497 gm.)	557
Poultry meat pies, frozen, commercial (Swanson brand)		
Chicken Pie	8-oz. pie (227 gm.)	503
Chicken—Deep Dish Pie	1-lb. pie (454 gm.)	731
Turkey Pie	8-oz. pie (227 gm.)	417
Turkey—Deep Dish Pie	1-lb. pie (454 gm.)	608

Poultry stuffing: See Breads, Miscellaneous, page 189.

SALAD DRESSINGS

		Calories
Blue and Roquefort cheese dressing, commercial		
Regular	1 tbsp. (16 gm.)	80
Low-calorie	1 tbsp. (16 gm.)	15
Cooked (boiled) salad dressing, home recipe	1 tbsp. (7 gm.)	30

		Calories
French dressing		
Commercial		
Regular	1 tbsp. (15 gm.)	60
Low-calorie (low fat)	1 tbsp. (15 gm.)	15
Low-calorie, with artificial sweetener (medium fat)	1 tbsp. (15 gm.)	25
Homemade	1 tbsp. (15 gm.)	95
Good Seasons Salad Dressings (prepared from mix)	1 tbsp. (16 gm.)	85
Italian salad dressing, commercial	1 tbsp. (15 gm.)	85
Mayonnaise, commercial	1 tbsp. (15 gm.)	105
	1 tsp. (5 gm.)	35
Miracle Whip	1 tbsp. (14 gm.)	69
Russian salad dressing, commercial	1 tbsp. (15 gm.)	75
Salad dressing, mayonnaise type, commercial		
Regular	1 tbsp. (15 gm.)	65
Low-calorie	1 tbsp. (15 gm.)	20
Thousand Island dressing, commercial		
Regular	1 tbsp. (15 gm.)	75
Low-calorie	1 tbsp. (15 gm.)	30

SAUCES

		Calories
Sauces for desserts		
Butterscotch sauce	2 tbsp. (1½ oz.)	205
Chocolate sauce	¼ cup (2¾ oz.)	175
Custard sauce	¼ cup (2½ oz.)	95
Dream Whip Whipped Topping Mix, prepared	1 tbsp. (5.6 gm.)	14

		Calories
Hard sauce	2 tbsp. (¾ oz.)	100
Lemon sauce	¼ cup (2 oz., scant)	130
Whipped cream (heavy), whipped		
Unsweetened	2 tbsp., level	55
Sweetened	2 tbsp., level	60
Whipped milk topping (evaporated milk base)	¼ cup	95
Whipped milk topping (instant nonfat dry milk base)	¼ cup	30
Sauces for meats, fish, and vegetables		
Barbecue sauce (without fat)	1 tbsp. (20 gm.)	18
Catsup	1 tbsp. (17 gm.)	20
Cheese sauce	¼ cup (75 gm.)	135
Chili sauce	1 tbsp. (17 gm.)	20
Cocktail sauce	2 tbsp.	35
Cranberry sauce, home prepared, unstrained	2 tbsp. (35 gm.)	60
Hollandaise sauce, true	¼ cup (50 gm.)	180
Lemon butter sauce (*maître d'hôtel* butter)	2 tbsp.	105
Meat sauce (restaurant)	1 tbsp.	20
Mushroom soup sauce	¼ cup	60
Raisin sauce	¼ cup (50 gm.)	130
Soy sauce	1 tbsp. (15 gm.)	10
Tartar sauce		
Regular	1 tbsp. (20 gm.)	105
Low-calorie	1 tbsp.	30
Tomato sauce, homemade	¼ cup (70 gm.)	80
White sauce, medium	¼ cup (66 gm.)	105
Worcestershire sauce	1 tbsp. (15 gm.)	12

SOUPS*

CANNED SOUPS

Canned soups and frozen canned soups are prepared by the addition of an equal volume of water or milk. One can of soup, prepared, makes three servings, 7 fluid ounces each (⅞ of a standard measuring cup). When soup is prepared with half whole milk, half water, use the calorie count for soup prepared with skim milk. For convenience, the calorie count for entire contents of can is given for several soups often used in recipes.

		Calories
Asparagus, Cream of (Campbell)		
Prepared with water	1 serving	70
Prepared with skim milk	1 serving	106
Prepared with whole milk	1 serving	138
Bean with Bacon (Campbell)		
Prepared with water	1 serving	133
Beef bouillon, broth, and consommé		
Prepared with water	1 serving	25
Black Bean (Campbell)		
Prepared with water	1 serving	80
Celery, Cream of (Heinz)		
Condensed	10½-oz. can	240
Prepared with water	1 serving	80
Prepared with skim milk	1 serving	115
Prepared with whole milk	1 serving	150
Cheese (Heinz)		
Prepared with water	1 serving	80
Prepared with skim milk	1 serving	115
Prepared with whole milk	1 serving	145

* The values on soups are based on data received from the Campbell Soup Company, February, 1966; from the H. J. Heinz Company, October, 1965; from Thomas J. Lipton, Inc., September, 1965.

		Calories
Chicken, Cream of (Campbell)		
Condensed	10½-oz. can	275
Prepared with water	1 serving	93
Prepared with skim milk	1 serving	129
Prepared with whole milk	1 serving	161
Chicken Noodle (Heinz)		
Prepared with water	1 serving	58
Chicken Vegetable (Heinz)		
Prepared with water	1 serving	60
Chicken with Rice (Heinz)		
Prepared with water	1 serving	45
Clam Chowder (Heinz)		
Prepared with water	1 serving	72
Green Pea (Campbell)		
Prepared with water	1 serving	116
Prepared with skim milk	1 serving	152
Prepared with whole milk	1 serving	184
Mushroom, Cream of (Heinz)		
Condensed	10½-oz. can	330
Prepared with water	1 serving	110
Prepared with skim milk	1 serving	145
Prepared with whole milk	1 serving	175
Onion (Campbell)		
Prepared with water	1 serving	29
Potato, Cream of (Campbell)		
Prepared with water	1 serving	59
Prepared with skim milk	1 serving	95
Prepared with whole milk	1 serving	127
Split Pea with Ham (Campbell)		
Prepared with water	1 serving	141
Prepared with skim milk	1 serving	177
Prepared with whole milk	1 serving	209
Tomato (Campbell)		
Condensed	10½-oz. can	205
Prepared with water	1 serving	69

		Calories
Prepared with skim milk	1 serving	105
Prepared with whole milk	1 serving	137
Vegetable (Made with Beef Stock) (Campbell)		
Prepared with water	1 serving	62
Vegetable Beef (Heinz)		
Prepared with water	1 serving	70

FROZEN CANNED SOUPS (Campbell)

Clam Chowder (New England style)		
Prepared with water	1 serving	108
Prepared with skim milk	1 serving	144
Prepared with whole milk	1 serving	176
Oyster Stew		
Prepared with water	1 serving	102
Prepared with skim milk	1 serving	138
Prepared with whole milk	1 serving	170
Shrimp, Cream of		
Prepared with water	1 serving	132
Prepared with skim milk	1 serving	168
Prepared with whole milk	1 serving	200

DEHYDRATED SOUPS

Lipton Mixes		
Chicken Noodle		
Prepared with water	8-oz. serving	54
Green Pea		
Prepared with water	8-oz. serving	128
Onion		
Prepared with water	8-oz. serving	35
Tomato		
Prepared with water	8-oz. serving	75

Calories

Red Kettle Mixes (Campbell)
  Beef, Old-Fashioned
    Prepared with water   8-oz. serving   87
  Potato, Cream of
    Prepared with water   8-oz. serving   79
    Prepared with water   8-oz. serving   108
      and skim milk
    Prepared with water   8-oz. serving   135
      and whole milk
  Vegetable with Noodles
    Prepared with water   8-oz. serving   69
Miscellaneous Soups
  Bean soup, home recipe   1 cup   260
  Bouillon, from cube   1 cup   5
  Jellied consommé   ½ cup   35
  Oyster stew, home recipe   1 serving   340
    8 oysters
    1 cup milk
    1 tbsp. butter
    seasonings

SUGARS, SWEETS

Calories

Candied fruits
  Candied apricots   1 average (1 oz.)   95
  Candied cherries   1 large (6 gm.)   20
  Candied citron   1 oz.   90
  Candied figs   1 oz.   85
  Candied ginger root   1 oz.   95
    (crystallized)
  Candied grapefruit, lemon,   1 oz.   90
    orange peel
  Candied pear   1 oz.   85
  Candied pineapple   1 oz.   90

Calories

Candy		
Butterscotch candy	1 small piece (5 gm.)	20
Candy corn	1 oz.	105
Caramels		
Plain or chocolate	1 average (10 gm.)	40
Plain or chocolate, with nuts	1 average (13 gm.)	55
Chocolate candy		
Bittersweet	1 oz.	135
Semisweet	1 oz.	145
Sweet	1 oz.	150
Milk chocolate		
Plain	1-oz. bar	150
With almonds	⅞-oz. bar	135
Chocolate creams	1 average (½ oz.)	60
Fondant	1 oz.	105
Fudge		
Chocolate	1 oz.	115
Chocolate, with nuts	1 oz.	120
Gum, chewing	1 stick (3 gm.)	10
Gumdrops	1 large or 8 small (12 gm.)	40
Hard candy	1 small piece (5 gm.)	20
Jelly beans	1 oz.	105
Life Savers	1 (2.3 gm.)	10
Marshmallows	1 average (6 gm.)	20
Mints		
Uncoated (after-dinner mints)	12, ⅜″ cubes (10 gm.)	36
Chocolate-covered	1 thin mint, 1¾″ diameter (10 gm.)	40
Peanut brittle	1 oz.	120
Jams, jellies, preserves		
Apple butter	1 tbsp. (18 gm.)	35

		Calories
Cranberry jelly, canned	1 tbsp. (20 gm.)	30
Jams, assorted	1 tbsp., level (20 gm.)	55
Jellies, assorted	1 tbsp., level (20 gm.)	55
Marmalade, citrus	1 tbsp. (20 gm.)	50
Dietetic jams, jellies	1 tsp. (7 gm.)	1⅓–4
Sirups and sugars		
Sirups		
Chocolate sirup		
Thin-type	1 tbsp. (20 gm.)	50
Fudge-type	1 oz.	95
Sirup, table blends (chiefly corn)	1 tbsp. (20 gm.)	60
Honey, strained	1 tbsp. (21 gm.)	65
Maple and maple-flavored sirups	1 tbsp. (20 gm.)	50
Molasses		
Light	1 tbsp. (20 gm.)	50
Blackstrap	1 tbsp. (20 gm.)	45
Sugars		
Brown sugar	1 cup (220 gm.)	820
	1 tbsp. (14 gm.)	50
Maple sugar	1 oz.	100
Powdered sugar, stirred before measuring	1 cup (128 gm.)	495
	1 tbsp. (8 gm.)	30
White sugar, granulated	1 cup (200 gm.)	770
	1 tbsp. (12.5 gm.)	48
	1 tsp., rounded (6 gm.)	25
Lump sugar	1 lump, 1⅛×¾×⅜″ (6 gm.)	25

VEGETABLES

		Calories
Artichokes, French		
Cooked	1 medium bud (100 gm., E.P.)	45

		Calories
Frozen*	2 hearts (3 oz.)	22
Asparagus, cooked	6 medium spears or ½ cup cut spears (100 gm.)	20
Beans		
Green beans, Italian, frozen	½ cup (3 oz.)	23
Lima beans, green		
Cooked	½ cup (80 gm.)	90
Frozen		
Baby limas	½ cup (94 gm.)	114
Fordhook limas	½ cup (94 gm.)	96
Navy beans, dried		
Cooked	½ cup (91 gm.)	105
Canned		
With pork and sweet sauce	½ cup (130 gm.)	195
With pork and tomato sauce	½ cup (130 gm.)	160
Red kidney beans, dried		
Cooked	½ cup (128 gm.)	150
Canned	½ cup (128 gm.)	115
Snap beans, cooked		
Green	¾ cup (94 gm.)	25
Yellow or wax	¾ cup (94 gm.)	20
Bean sprouts, Mung, canned, drained	1 cup (4 oz.)	32
Beets		
Cooked, diced	½ cup (82 gm.)	25
Canned, drained, diced	½ cup (82 gm.)	30
Beet greens, cooked	½ cup (72 gm.)	15
Broccoli, cooked	⅔ cup or 1 large stalk (100 gm.)	25
Brussels sprouts, cooked	½ cup (about 5) (65 gm.)	25

* Data on frozen vegetables by Birds Eye.

		Calories
Cabbage		
Raw	1 wedge, 3½×4½" (100 gm.)	25
Shredded	½ cup (50 gm.)	12
Coleslaw		
With mayonnaise	½ cup (60 gm.)	85
With commercial salad dressing (mayonnaise type)	½ cup (60 gm.)	60
Cooked	¾ cup (128 gm.)	25
Carrots		
Raw	1, 5½×1" or ½ cup, grated (50 gm.)	20
Cooked or canned, diced	½ cup (72 gm.)	20
Carrot juice	½ cup (4 fluid oz.)	50
Cauliflower		
Raw	⅓ cup flower buds (33 gm.)	10
Cooked	½ cup (60 gm.)	15
Celery		
Raw	3 small inner stalks (59 gm.)	10
Pieces, diced	1 cup (100 gm.)	17
Cooked, diced	½ cup (65 gm.)	10
Chard, Swiss, cooked	½ cup (72 gm.)	15
Chicory (French or Belgian endive), raw	2-oz. head	10
Chives, raw, chopped	1 tbsp. (7 gm.)	2
Collards, cooked	½ cup (95 gm.)	30
Corn, sweet		
Cooked	1 ear, 5" long (140 gm. incl. cob)	70
	½ cup kernels (82 gm.)	75

Calories

Canned		
Cream style	½ cup (128 gm.)	105
Kernels, drained	½ cup (82 gm.)	70
Cucumbers, raw, pared	1, 7½×2″ (207 gm.)	30
	⅛″ slice (8 gm.)	1
Dandelion greens, cooked	½ cup (90 gm.)	30
Eggplant, raw	2 slices, 3½″ diameter × ½″ or 1 cup, diced (100 gm.)	25
Endive, curly	2 oz.	10
Escarole	2 oz.	10
Garlic cloves	1 (2 gm.)	3
Kale, cooked (leaves including stems)	½ cup (55 gm.)	15
Lettuce		
Boston	1 head, 4″ diameter (220 gm.)	30
Iceberg	1 head, 4¾″ diameter (1 lb.)	60
	1 wedge, ¼ head (4 oz.)	15
	2 to 3 leaves (38 gm.)	5
Mixed vegetables, frozen	½ cup (94 gm.)	61
Mushrooms		
Raw	2 jumbo or 4 large or 10 small (100 gm.)	28
Canned (including liquid)	½ cup (122 gm.)	20
Canned, drained	½ cup (85 gm.)	28
Mustard greens, cooked	½ cup (70 gm.)	15
Okra, cooked	8 pods, 3″ long (85 gm.)	25
Onions, mature		
Raw	1, 2½″ diameter (110 gm.)	40

		Calories
Chopped	1 tbsp. (10 gm.)	4
Cooked, whole	½ cup (2 to 3 small) (105 gm.)	30
Onions, young green	6 small (50 gm.)	20
Parsley	10 sprigs (10 gm.)	5
Chopped	1 tbsp. (3.5 gm.)	1
Parsnips, cooked	½ cup (78 gm.)	50
Peas, green (young)		
Cooked	½ cup (80 gm.)	55
Canned, drained	½ cup (80 gm.)	70
Peas and carrots, frozen	½ cup (94 gm.)	52
Peppers, green, raw	1 medium (62 gm.)	15
Chopped	1 tbsp. (10 gm.)	2
Pimientos, canned	1 medium (38 gm.)	10
Potatoes, white, cooked		
Baked in skin	1 medium, 2½″ diameter (99 gm.)	90
Boiled in skin	1, peeled (136 gm.)	105
Boiled, pared before cooking	1 (122 gm.)	80
Cooked, diced	1 cup (132 gm.)	100
French-fried	10 pieces, 2×½×½″ (57 gm.)	155
Frozen	17 pieces (3 oz.)	145
Hash-browned	½ cup (98 gm.)	225
Mashed, milk and table fat added	½ cup (98 gm.)	90
Potato chips	10 medium, 2″ diameter (20 gm.)	115
Potato salad	½ cup (125 gm.)	180
Pumpkin, canned	1 cup (228 gm.)	75
Radishes, raw (without tops)	4 small (40 gm.)	5
Romaine	3 medium leaves (1 oz.)	5
Rutabagas, cooked	½ cup (78 gm.)	25
Sauerkraut, canned, including liquid	1 cup (235 gm.)	45
Spinach, cooked	½ cup (90 gm.)	20

		Calories
Squash, summer, cooked, diced	½ cup (105 gm.)	15
Squash, winter		
Baked, mashed	½ cup (102 gm.)	65
Frozen	½ cup (4 oz.)	43
Acorn squash, baked	½ medium (91 gm.)	50
Succotash, frozen	½ cup (94 gm.)	90
Sweet potatoes, cooked		
Baked in skin	1 (110 gm.)	155
Boiled in skin	1 (147 gm.)	170
Candied	1, 3½×2¼" (175 gm.)	295
Canned, vacuum or solid pack	½ cup (109 gm.)	120
Tomatoes		
Raw	1 medium, 2×2½" (150 gm.)	35
	1 small (110 gm.)	25
Canned	½ cup (121 gm.)	25
Cooked	½ cup (121 gm.)	30
Tomato juice, canned or bottled	½ cup (121 gm.)	25
Turnips, white, cooked, diced	½ cup (78 gm.)	20
Turnip greens, cooked	½ cup (72 gm.)	15
Vegetable juice cocktail, canned	½ cup (4 fluid oz.)	20
Water chestnuts	1 (8.5 gm.)	7
Watercress, raw	10 sprigs (10 gm.)	2

MISCELLANEOUS FOODS

		Calories
Baking powder	1 tsp. (4 gm.)	5
Bouillon cubes	⅝" cube (4 gm.)	5

Calories

Chocolate		
Unsweetened chocolate (bitter chocolate)	1 oz.	140–145
Semisweet chocolate	1 oz.	130–145
Sweet cooking chocolate	1 oz.	130–150
Cocoa, dry powder	1 tbsp., level (7 gm.)	21
Cocoa and chocolate beverage powders (commercial mixes)		
Hot chocolate mix	1 oz.	115
Instant cocoa mix	1 oz.	105
	2 heaping tsp. (⅔ oz.; amount for 1 cup beverage)	70
Cornstarch	1 tbsp. (8 gm.)	30
Dream Whip Whipped Topping Mix, dry form	1 envelope (2 oz.)	360
Gelatin, dry		
Unflavored gelatin	1 tbsp. (10 gm.)	35
	1 envelope (8 gm.)	28
Jell-O Fruit Flavor Gelatin	3-oz. package (85 gm.)	330
Jello-O Salad Gelatin	3-oz. package (85 gm.)	300
D-Zerta Low Calorie Gelatin Dessert	1 envelope (11.2 gm.)	36
Malted milk, dry powder, plain or chocolate	1 oz. (approx. 2 tbsp.)	115
	2 heaping tsp. (¾ oz.; amount for 1 cup beverage)	87
Popcorn, popped, plain	1 cup (14 gm.)	55
Postum, Instant, dry powder	1 tsp., rounded (5.5 gm.)	14
Pudding mixes		
D-Zerta Low Calorie Pudding & Pie Filling		
Butterscotch flavor	1 envelope (18.9 gm.)	62

		Calories
Chocolate flavor	1 envelope (18.9 gm.)	55
Vanilla flavor	1 envelope (18.9 gm.)	64
Pudding & Pie Filling Mix (chocolate)	4 oz. package (4 servings)	409
Instant Pudding Mix	4½-oz. package (4 to 5 servings)	455
Sherry, cooking	¼ cup (2 oz.)	80
Sunflower seed kernels	¼ cup (1 oz.)	160
Tapioca, dry	1 tbsp. (10 gm.)	35
Vanilla extract	1 tsp.	8
Vinegar	1 tbsp. (15 gm.)	2
Yeast, baker's		
Compressed	1 oz.	25
Dry, active	1 oz.	80
Yeast, brewer's, dry	1 tbsp. (8 gm.)	25

TABLE 1

DESIRABLE WEIGHTS FOR HEIGHT

Height (inches)	WEIGHTS OF MEN			WEIGHTS OF WOMEN		
	Low Pounds	Median Pounds	High Pounds	Low Pounds	Median Pounds	High Pounds
60	......	......	......	100	109	118
61	......	......	......	104	112	121
62	......	......	......	107	115	125
63	118	129	141	110	118	128
64	122	133	145	113	122	132
65	126	137	149	116	125	135
66	130	142	155	120	129	139
67	134	147	161	123	132	142
68	139	151	166	126	136	146
69	143	155	170	130	140	151
70	147	159	174	133	144	156
71	150	163	178	137	148	161
72	154	167	183	141	152	166
73	158	171	188	......	......	......
74	162	175	192	......	......	......
75	165	178	195	......	......	......

Taken from "Trends in Heights and Weights," Milicent L. Hathaway, 1959 Yearbook of Agriculture, FOOD, U. S. Government Printing Office, Washington, D.C. Heights and weights are without shoes and other clothing.

TABLE 2

RECOMMENDED DAILY DIETARY ALLOWANCES

DESIGNED FOR THE MAINTENANCE OF GOOD NUTRITION OF HEALTHY PERSONS IN THE U.S.A.

(Allowances are intended for persons normally active and living in a temperate climate)

	Age in Years from	to	Weight in Pounds	Height in Inches	Food Energy Units Calories	Protein Grams	Calcium Grams	Iron Milligrams	Vitamin A International Units	Thiamine Milligrams	Riboflavin Milligrams	Ascorbic Acid Milligrams	Vitamin D International Units
Men	18	35	154	69	2900	70	.8	10	5000	1.2	1.7	70	
	35	55	154	69	2600	70	.8	10	5000	1.0	1.6	70	
	55	75	154	69	2200	70	.8	10	5000	.9	1.3	70	
Women	18	35	128	64	2100	58	.8	15	5000	.8	1.3	70	
	35	55	128	64	1900	58	.8	15	5000	.8	1.2	70	
	55	75	128	64	1600	58	.8	10	5000	.8	1.2	70	
Pregnant (2nd and 3rd trimester)					+200	78	1.3	20	6000	1.0	1.6	100	400
Lactating					+1000	98	1.3	20	9000	1.2	1.9	100	400
Children	1	3	29	34	1300	32	.6	8	2000	.5	.8	40	400
	3	6	40	42	1600	40	.8	10	2500	.6	1.0	50	400
	6	9	53	43	2000	52	.8	12	3500	.8	1.3	60	400
Boys	9	12	72	55	2400	60	1.1	15	4500	1.0	1.4	70	400
	12	15	98	61	3000	75	1.4	15	5000	1.2	1.8	80	400
	15	18	134	68	3400	85	1.4	15	5000	1.4	2.0	80	400
Girls	9	12	72	55	2200	55	1.1	15	4500	.9	1.3	80	400
	12	15	103	62	2500	62	1.3	15	5000	1.0	1.5	80	400
	15	18	117	64	2300	58	1.3	15	5000	.9	1.3	70	400

Adapted from *Recommended Dietary Allowances*, sixth revised edition, 1964. National Academy of Sciences, National Research Council, Washington, D.C.

The recommended allowances can be attained with a variety of common foods, providing other nutrients for which human requirements have been less well defined.

The Food and Drug Administration has established minimum daily requirements for vitamins and minerals which are the basis for label statements on foods.

TABLE 3

FOOD COMPOSITION TABLE FOR SHORT METHOD OF DIETARY ANALYSIS (3RD REVISION)

Food and Approximate Measure	Weight, gm	Food Energy, Cal.	Protein, gm
Milk, cheese, cream; related products			
Cheese: blue, cheddar (1 cu in., 17 gm),			
cheddar process (1 oz), Swiss (1 oz)	30	105	6
cottage (from skim) creamed (½ c)	115	120	16
Cream: half-and-half (cream and milk) (2 tbsp)			
For light whipping add 1 pat butter	30	40	1
Milk: whole (3.5% fat) (1 c)	245	160	9
fluid, nonfat (skim) and buttermilk (from skim)	245	90	9
milk beverages, (1 c) cocoa, chocolate drink made with skim milk. For malted milk add 4 tbsp half-and-half (270 gm)	245	210	8
milk desserts, custard (1 c) 248 gm, ice cream (8 fl oz) 142 gm		290	8
cornstarch pudding (248 gm), ice milk (1 c) 187 gm		280	9
White sauce, med (½ c)	130	215	5
Egg: 1 large	50	80	6
Meat, poultry, fish, shellfish, related products			
Beef, lamb, veal: lean and fat, cooked, inc. corned beef (3 oz) (all cuts)	85	245	22
lean only, cooked; dried beef (2+ oz) (all cuts)	65	140	20
Beef, relatively fat, such as steak and rib, cooked (3 oz)	85	350	18
Liver: beef, fried (2 oz)	55	130	15
Pork, lean & fat, cooked (3 oz) (all cuts)	85	325	20
lean only, cooked (2+ oz) (all cuts)	60	150	18
ham, light cure, lean & fat, roasted (3 oz)	85	245	18
Luncheon meats: bologna (2 sl), pork sausage, cooked (2 oz), frankfurter (1), bacon, broiled or fried crisp (3 sl)		185	9
Poultry			
chicken: flesh only, broiled (3 oz)	85	115	20
fried (2+ oz)	75	170	24
turkey, light & dark, roasted (3 oz)	85	160	27
Fish and shellfish			
salmon (3 oz) (canned)	85	130	17
fish sticks, breaded, cooked (3–4)	75	130	13
mackerel, halibut, cooked	85	175	19
bluefish, haddock, herring, perch, shad, cooked (tuna canned in oil, 20 gm)	85	160	19
clams, canned; crabmeat, canned; lobster; oyster, raw; scallop; shrimp, canned	85	75	14
Mature dry beans and peas, nuts, peanuts, related products			
Beans: white with pork and tomato, canned (1 c)	260	320	16
red (128 gm), lima (96 gm), cowpeas (125 gm), cooked (½ c)		125	8

Fat, gm	Carbo- hy- drate, gm	Cal- cium, mg	Iron, mg	Vita- min A Value, IU	Thia- mine, mg	Ribo- flavin, mg	Niacin, mg	Ascor- bic Acid, mg
9	1	165	0.2	345	0.01	0.12	trace	0
5	3	105	0.4	190	0.04	0.28	0.1	0
4	2	30	trace	145	0.01	0.04	trace	trace
9	12	285	0.1	350	0.08	0.42	0.1	2
trace	13	300	trace	–	0.10	0.44	0.2	2
8	26	280	0.6	300	0.09	0.43	0.3	trace
17	29	210	0.4	785	0.07	0.34	0.1	1
10	40	290	0.1	390	0.08	0.41	0.3	2
16	12	150	0.2	610	0.06	0.22	0.3	trace
6	trace	25	1.2	590	0.06	0.15	trace	0
16	0	10	2.9	25	0.06	0.19	4.2	0
5	0	10	2.4	10	0.05	0.16	3.4	0
30	0	10	2.4	60	0.05	0.14	3.5	0
6	3	5	5.0	30,280	0.15	2.37	9.4	15
24	0	10	2.6	0	0.62	0.20	4.2	0
8	0	5	2.2	0	0.57	0.19	3.2	0
19	0	10	2.2	0	0.40	0.16	3.1	0
16	–	5	1.3	–	0.21	0.12	1.7	0
3	0	10	1.4	80	0.05	0.16	7.4	0
6	1	10	1.6	85	0.05	0.23	8.3	0
5	0	–	1.5	–	0.03	0.15	6.5	0
5	0	165	0.7	60	0.03	0.16	6.8	0
7	5	10	0.3	–	0.03	0.05	1.2	0
10	0	10	0.8	515	0.08	0.15	6.8	0
8	2	20	1.0	60	0.06	0.11	4.4	0
1	2	65	2.5	65	0.10	0.08	1.5	0
7	50	140	4.7	340	0.20	0.08	1.5	5
–	25	35	2.5	5	0.13	0.06	0.7	–

TABLE 3 (continued)

FOOD COMPOSITION TABLE FOR SHORT
METHOD OF DIETARY ANALYSIS

Food and Approximate Measure	Weight, gm	Food Energy, Cal.	Protein, gm
Nuts: almonds (12), cashews (8), peanuts (1 tbsp), peanut butter (1 tbsp), pecans (12), English walnuts (2 tbsp), coconut (¼ c)	15	95	3
Vegetables and vegetable products			
Asparagus, cooked, cut spears (⅔ c)	115	25	3
Beans: green (½ c) cooked 60 gm; canned 120 gm		15	1
Lima, immature, cooked (½ c)	80	90	6
Broccoli spears, cooked (⅔ c)	100	25	3
Brussels sprouts, cooked (⅔ c)	85	30	3
Cabbage (110 gm); cauliflower, cooked (80 gm); and sauerkraut, canned (150 gm) (reduce ascorbic acid value by one-third for kraut) (⅔ c)		20	1
Carrots, cooked (⅔ c)	95	30	1
Corn, 1 ear, cooked (140 gm); canned (130 gm) (½ c)		75	2
Leafy greens: collards (125 gm), dandelions (120 gm), kale (75 gm), mustard (95 gm), spinach (120 gm), turnip (100 gm cooked, 150 gm canned) (⅔ c cooked and canned) (reduce ascorbic acid one-half for canned)		30	3
Peas, green (½ c)	80	60	4
Potatoes—baked, boiled (100 gm), 10 pc French fried (55 gm) (for fried, add 1 tbsp cooking oil)		85	3
Pumpkin, canned (½ c)	115	40	1
Squash, winter, canned (½ c)	100	65	2
Sweet potato, canned (½ c)	110	120	2
Tomato, 1 raw, ⅔ c canned, ⅔ c juice	150	35	2
Tomato catsup (2 tbsp)	35	30	1
Other, cooked (beets, mushrooms, onions, turnips) (½ c)	95	25	1
Others commonly served raw, cabbage (½ c, 50 gm), celery (3 sm stalks, 40 gm), cucumber (¼ med, 50 gm), green pepper (½, 30 gm), radishes (5, 40 gm)		10	trace
carrots, raw (½ carrot)	25	10	trace
lettuce leaves (2 lg)	50	10	1
Fruits and fruit products			
Cantaloupe (½ med)	385	60	1
Citrus and strawberries: orange (1), grapefruit (½), juice (½ c), strawberries (½ c), lemon (1), tangerine (1)		50	1
Yellow, fresh: apricots (3), peach (2 med); canned fruit and juice (½ c) or dried, cooked, unsweetened: apricot, peaches (½ c)		85	–

Fat, gm	Carbo- hy- drate, gm	Cal- cium, mg	Iron, mg	Vita- min A Value, IU	Thia- mine, mg	Ribo- flavin, mg	Niacin, mg	Ascor- bic Acid, mg
8	4	15	0.5	5	0.05	0.04	0.9	–
trace	4	25	0.7	1,055	0.19	0.20	1.6	30
trace	3	30	0.4	340	0.04	0.06	0.3	8
1	16	40	2.0	225	0.14	0.08	1.0	14
trace	4	90	0.8	2,500	0.09	0.20	0.8	90
trace	5	30	1.0	450	0.07	0.12	0.7	75
trace	4	35	0.5	80	0.05	0.05	0.3	37
trace	7	30	0.6	10,145	0.05	0.05	0.5	6
trace	18	5	0.4	315	0.06	0.06	1.1	6
trace	5	175	1.8	8,570	0.11	0.18	0.8	45
1	10	20	1.4	430	0.22	0.09	1.8	16
trace	30	10	0.7	trace	0.08	0.04	1.5	16
1	9	30	0.5	7,295	0.03	0.06	0.6	6
1	16	30	0.8	4,305	0.05	0.14	0.7	14
–	27	25	0.8	8,500	0.05	0.05	0.7	15
trace	7	14	0.8	1,350	0.10	0.06	1.0	29
trace	8	10	0.2	480	0.04	0.02	0.6	6
–	5	20	0.5	15	0.02	0.10	0.7	7
trace	2	15	0.3	100	0.03	0.03	0.2	20
trace	2	10	0.2	2,750	0.02	0.02	0.2	2
trace	2	34	0.7	950	0.03	0.04	0.2	9
trace	14	25	0.8	6,540	0.08	0.06	1.2	63
–	13	25	0.4	165	0.08	0.03	0.3	55
–	22	10	1.1	1,005	0.01	0.05	1.0	5

TABLE 3 (continued)

FOOD COMPOSITION TABLE FOR SHORT METHOD OF DIETARY ANALYSIS

Food and Approximate Measure	Weight, gm	Food Energy, Cal.	Pro-tein, gm
Other, dried: dates, pitted (4), figs (2), raisins (¼ c)	40	120	1
Other, fresh: apple (1), banana (1), figs (3), pear (1)		80	–
Fruit pie: to 1 serving fruit add 1 tbsp flour, 2 tbsp sugar, 1 tbsp fat			
Grain products			
Enriched and whole grain: bread (1 sl, 23 gm), biscuit (½), cooked cereals (½ c), prepared cereals (1 oz), Graham crackers (2 lg), macaroni, noodles, spaghetti (½ c, cooked), pancake (1, 27 gm), roll (½), waffle (½, 38 gm)		65	2
Unenriched: bread (1 sl, 23 gm), cooked cereal (½ c), macaroni, noodles, spaghetti (½ c), popcorn (½ c), pretzel sticks, small (15), roll (½)		65	2
Desserts			
Cake, plain (1 pc), doughnut (1). For iced cake or doughnut add value for sugar (1 tbsp). For chocolate cake add chocolate (30 gm)	45	145	2
Cookies, plain (1)	25	120	1
Piecrust, single crust (⅐ shell)	20	95	1
Flour, white, enriched (1 tbsp)	7	25	1
Fats and oils			
Butter, margarine (1 pat, ½ tbsp)	7	50	trace
Fats and oils, cooking (1 tbsp), French dressing (2 tbsp)	14	125	0
Salad dressing, mayonnaise type (1 tbsp)	15	80	trace
Sugars, sweets			
Candy, plain (½ oz), jam and jelly (1 tbsp), sirup (1 tbsp), gelatin dessert, plain (½ c), beverages, carbonated (1 c)		60	0
Chocolate fudge (1 oz), chocolate sirup (3 tbsp)		125	1
Molasses (1 tbsp), caramel (⅓ oz)		40	trace
Sugar (1 tbsp)	12	45	0
Miscellaneous			
Chocolate, bitter (1 oz)	30	145	3
Sherbet (½ c)	96	130	1
Soups: bean, pea (green) (1 c)		150	7
noodle, beef, chicken (1 c)		65	4
clam chowder, minestrone, tomato, vegetable (1 c)		90	3

The short method of figuring food values is satisfactory from the standpoint of accuracy. The saving in time is considerable.

Fat, gm	Carbo-hy-drate, gm	Cal-cium, mg	Iron, mg	Vita-min A Value, IU	Thia-mine, mg	Ribo-flavin, mg	Niacin, mg	Ascor-bic Acid, mg
–	31	35	1.4	20	0.04	0.04	0.5	–
–	21	15	0.5	140	0.04	0.03	0.2	6
1	16	20	0.6	10	0.09	0.05	0.7	–
1	16	10	0.3	5	0.02	0.02	0.3	–
5	24	30	0.4	65	0.02	0.05	0.2	–
5	18	10	0.2	20	0.01	0.01	0.1	–
6	8	3	0.3	0	0.04	0.03	0.3	–
trace	5	1	0.2	0	0.03	0.02	0.2	0
6	trace	1	0	230	–	–	–	–
14	0	0	0	0	0	0	0	0
9	1	2	0.1	45	trace	trace	trace	0
0	14	3	0.1	trace	trace	trace	trace	trace
2	30	15	0.6	10	trace	0.02	0.1	trace
trace	8	20	0.3	trace	trace	trace	trace	trace
0	12	0	trace	0	0	0	0	0
15	8	20	1.9	20	0.01	0.07	0.4	0
1	30	15	trace	55	0.01	0.03	trace	2
4	22	50	1.6	495	0.09	0.06	1.0	4
2	7	10	0.7	50	0.03	0.04	0.9	trace
2	14	25	0.9	1,880	0.05	0.04	1.1	3

3rd Revision by Garrett, Leichsenring and Wilson, in press, J. American Dietetic Association, 1966. Source material for food values: Agriculture Handbook 8, revised 1963.

RECOMMENDED REFERENCES

Food Becomes You, by Dr. Ruth Leverton, third edition. Ames, Iowa: Iowa State University Press, 1965.

Handbook of Diet Therapy, by Dorothea Turner, third edition, for The American Dietetic Association. Chicago: The University of Chicago Press, 1965.

The Heinz Handbook of Nutrition, by Dr. Benjamin T. Burton, second edition. New York: McGraw-Hill Book Company, Inc., 1965.

Lessons on Meat, Source Book on Meat for Professional and Classroom Reference, second edition. Chicago: The National Live Stock and Meat Board, 1965.

Nutrition and Physical Fitness, by L. Jean Bogert, seventh edition. Philadelphia: W. B. Saunders Company, 1960.

Nutrition in Health and Disease, by Lenna F. Cooper, Edith M. Barber, Helen S. Mitchell, Henderika Rynbergen, Jessie C. Greene, fourteenth edition. Philadelphia: J. B. Lippincott Company, 1963.

Nutrition Science and You, by Dr. Olaf Mickelson. Englewood Cliffs, N.J.: Scholastic Book Services, 1964.

The Overweight Society, by Peter Weyden. New York: The William Morrow Company, 1965.

Reduce and Stay Reduced, by Dr. Norman Jolliffe. New York: Simon & Schuster, 1957.

Your Heart Has Nine Lives, by Alton Blakeslee and Dr. Jeremiah Stamler. Englewood Cliffs, N.J.: Prentice-Hall, Inc., 1963.

Your Weight and How to Control It, edited by Dr. Morris Fishbein. Garden City, N.Y.: Doubleday & Company, 1963.

TABLE OF SUGAR EQUIVALENCIES*

Sugar	Sweetener
1 tsp.	⅛ tsp. Sucaryl solution or 1 tablet 2 drops Sweeta ⅛ tsp. Sweet * 10
1 tbsp. (3 tsp.)	⅜ tsp. Sucaryl solution or 3 tablets 6 drops Sweeta ⅜ tsp. Sweet * 10
¼ cup (4 tbsp.)	1½ tsp. Sucaryl solution or 12 tablets 24 drops Sweeta (⅛ tsp.) 1 tsp. Sweet * 10
⅓ cup	2 tsp. Sucaryl solution or 16 tablets 32 drops Sweeta 1⅓ tsp. Sweet * 10
1 cup	2 tbsp. Sucaryl solution or 48 tablets ½ tsp. Sweeta 4 tsp. Sweet * 10

* This Table of Sugar Equivalencies is not exhaustive. For other sweeteners on the market, directions for use will be found on the container.

TABLE OF MEASUREMENT EQUIVALENTS

1 quart	4 cups
1 cup	8 fluid ounces
	½ pint
	16 tablespoons
½ cup	8 tablespoons
⅓ cup	5⅓ tablespoons
¼ cup	4 tablespoons
2 tablespoons	1 fluid ounce
1 tablespoon	3 teaspoons

Standard-size measuring cup used.

Index

K4